Chef Verati

MY *Ideal* RECIPES

250 SCRUMPTIOUS WAYS TO ENJOY YOUR MEALS

PHASE 1-2

Original Title: My Ideal Recipes
© COPYRIGHT 2011 – LABORATOIRES C.O.P. INC.
- ALL RIGHTS RESERVED
®/TM/MD/MC Trade marks of LABORATOIRES C.O.P. INC.

Author: Daniel Verati

Editor: Wendi Eeet

Graphic Design: www.oragecommunication.com

Original Photographs : Studio Photo Daniel Osborne
Photos : © fotolia © istockphoto

Printed in Canada

Table of Contents

Author's Preface

After spending 25 years managing kitchen personnel and creating fine dishes all over the world, I came close to a full stop in 2007 when I was diagnosed with a heart condition. That year turned out to be a decisive one that brought profound change into my life. Standing at a mere 5'8'' and tipping the scale at 283 pounds, I realized that I had been overweight for the last 18 years of my life and I knew I could no longer continue this way if I wanted to see my children grow up.

At the time, I was teaching at the Cordon Bleu Culinary Arts Institute in Ottawa (Canada), which can be a tough environment to be in when one wants to loose weight and improve eating habits! I became acutely aware that I needed a good weight-loss regimen that included a dietary "rehabilitation" program to avoid the legendary "yo-yo effect". At the time, my childhood and closest friend, Olivier Benloulou, was changing lives with the Ideal Protein protocol, so I listened to his advice and started the program, knowing full well that it was time for me to take control over my life.

Five months later and 100 pounds lighter, I quit my job at the Cordon Bleu Ottawa, ready to take on new and exciting challenges at Ideal Protein.

The Ideal Protein weigh loss program proved to be a very enriching and invigorating experience and I decided to use my skills and my passion for good food to make a longtime dream come true. It became clear to me that I wanted to share the delectable creations that I had developed while I was on the program.

Have a look at a few recipes and you will see how eating well doesn't have to be boring or tasteless! All the recipes are extremely easy to prepare. The results are savory and full of incomparable aromas and flavors that will please the taste buds of even the most discriminating epicurean.

I have poured my heart and soul into each recipe over many months of trial and refinement, and none of this would have been possible without the support of my family. I would like to give special thanks to my wife, Lise, and our two daughters, Alizé and Michèle, who graciously sacrificed precious family time so that I could invest my energies into this book.

I also want to thank my precious collaborators Juliane and Francine, Daniel Osborne and his team and Claude Goyard. Heartfelt thanks to Wendi Eeet for her devotion during the editing process and to Guylaine Sheehy for her inspiring graphic design.

And finally, I want to thank Olivier and Dr. Tran for their trust and encouragement.

Daniel Verati

Daniel Verati
Chef, Ideal Protein

Foreward

My childhood friend Dan (Chef Verati) and I started our careers in somewhat similar areas. Driven by his passion for food, Dan travelled the world as a French Chef sharing his skills and teaching them to others.

As for me, I became a businessman and the owner of a five-star French restaurant where I put my talents to work. It had always been my dream to create an atmos¬phere where people could enjoy special evenings together while dining on fine food. I wanted this to be more than just "eating out"; I wanted to create an experience.

Eventually my career path led me to Ideal Protein. Though I am now focused on a very different goal, one that is more about helping individuals, it is still very important to me that families enjoy their time together at the dinner table and not sacrifice the experience of gourmet dining.

Today, Dan has focused his creativity on what we teach with the Ideal Protein Method and has created a recipe book that can help people can do just that: share wonderful dishes together! I am proud that Dan's passion is showcased as part of the Ideal Protein Method and I hope you will enjoy every one of these dishes as much as I did with my family.

Thank you Dan for sharing your talents with the Ideal Protein family.

Olivier Benloulou

Olivier Benloulou
President & CEO
Ideal Protein

Soups, salads and eggs

Tips and tricks

All recipes provide for 4 servings.

Soups are an easy way to ensure you eat your two cups of mandatory vegetables with your meal.

In fact, all the recipes in all sections contain two cups of vegetables that are required while on the protocol.

When preparing basil pesto, always make the batch in double or triple volume. You may freeze it in ice cube containers to use at a later date. Pesto is a great addition to any dish.

You may substitute Quail eggs in any dish with Chicken eggs.

Using crab claws in their shell is a simple nice-looking technique which is also very flavorful.

Hey, any questions?
Find us on Chef Verati facebook page
or write chefverati@idealprotein.com

Bon appétit!

Coleslaw Salad p.27

"Tortilla" Green Soup

1 1/2	pounds skinless chicken breasts cooked and shredded	1 1/2	cups Walden Farms Tomato and Basil Sauce
8	cups fat-free chicken stock	1	tablespoon olive oil
2	packets Ideal Protein Pancakes prepared	4	tablespoons hot sauce
3	cups celery root small cubes	1	bay leaf
2	cups spinach	1	teaspoon chili powder
1 1/2	cups green onions chopped		teaspoon cumin
1	cup leek		sea salt to taste
5	tablespoons garlic minced		pepper to taste
3	tablespoons cilantro chopped		
3	tablespoons chives chopped		

Slowly cook green onions, leek and garlic in olive oil. Add celery root. Add spices, sauce and stock. Cook on low for 45 minutes.
Preheat oven to 400 degrees.

Prepare four 8" diameter pancakes adding 1 tablespoon of cilantro. Cut into strips and place on baking sheet. Brush lightly with oil and bake for 5 to 10 minutes or until crisp. Just before serving, add chicken, sprinkle soup with pancake strips and remaining cilantro.

Per Serving: 350 Calories; 6g Fat; 65g Protein; 25g Carbohydrate

Italian Broccoli Soup

3/4	pound prosciutto
4	eggs
4	cups chicken stock
8	cups frozen broccoli cut in 1" pieces
1	teaspoon garlic crushed
2	teaspoons Walden Farms Italian Dressing
1	teaspoon olive oil

Sauté prosciutto in a pan at medium-high temperature. Add garlic. Add chicken stock and 4 cups of water. Cover and bring to a boil then simmer. Add broccoli and return to a boil. Simmer for 12 minutes or until broccoli is tender. Add dressing.

Whisk eggs and slowly pour into the soup. This will result in beautiful egg filaments. Simmer for another minute. Serve immediately.

Per Serving: 354 Calories; 14g Fat; 40g Protein; 17g Carbohydrate

Soups, salads and eggs

"Tortilla" Green Soup

Asparagus Soup

1 1/2	pounds ham slices, extra lean julienned	2	teaspoons olive oil
6	cups chicken stock	2	teaspoons caraway seeds
6	cups asparagus		sea salt to taste
2	cups green onions		pepper to taste
2	tablespoons dill		

Cut asparagus into small pieces. Set tips aside.
Cook asparagus tips in boiling stock. Set aside.

Slowly cook green onions and caraway in olive oil. Add asparagus pieces. Add stock.
Cook for 45 minutes. Blend. Pass the soup through a sieve. Add ham and cooked
asparagus tips.

Serve very hot.

Per Serving: 355 Calories; 12g Fat; 40g Protein; 17g Carbohydrate

....

Broccoli Soup

1 1/2	pounds ham slice, extra lean finely diced	2	tablespoons olive oil
8	cups broccoli chopped stems and florets separated	2	tablespoons onion powder
		1	tablespoon caraway seed
2	ounces fennel chopped		hot sauce to taste
1	ounce celery stalks chopped		sea salt to taste
2	cloves garlic peeled		pepper to taste
1	tablespoon Walden Farms Alfredo Sauce		

Heat pan and add olive oil. Add broccoli stems, garlic, onion powder, fennel and celery.
Cook for 3 minutes, do not allow to brown. Add 6 cups of water, cover and let simmer on
medium heat for 30 minutes. Bring to a boil. Add broccoli florets and simmer for 5 minutes.
Remove broccoli florets from soup (keep the rest of the vegetables in the soup). Add
Alfredo sauce to soup and return to a boil. Purée all ingredients from the pot, than return
to pot.

Toast caraway seeds and add to soup. Season with hot sauce, salt and pepper.
Add ham and broccoli florets just before serving.

Per Serving: 359 Calories; 16g Fat; 38g Protein; 14g Carbohydrate

Soups, salads and eggs

Asparagus Soup

Cauliflower and Curry Soup

1 1/4	pounds smoked ham
8	cups chicken stock
8	cups cauliflower chopped
1/2	cup Walden Farms Alfredo Sauce
1	teaspoon curry paste
1	tablespoon olive oil

Combine chicken stock, cauliflower, curry and bring to a boil. Simmer for 30 minutes or until cooked. Purée. Return puree to pot and add Alfredo sauce. Simmer for 5 minutes. In hot olive oil, sauté the smoked ham until golden. Add to soup.

Serve very hot.

Per Serving: 353 Calories; 15g Fat; 35g Protein; 15g Carbohydrate

Chicken and Leek Soup

1 1/2	pounds chicken breast cooked
4	cups chicken stock
2	cups celery root cubed small
6	cups leek cut very thin
2	teaspoons olive oil
	sea salt to taste
	cayenne pepper to taste

Slowly sauté leek in olive oil. Add the celery root. Season with sea salt and cayenne pepper. Add stock, 4 cup of water and simmer until vegetable are tender.
Add cubed chicken breast.

Serve very hot.

Per Serving: 367 Calories; 16g Fat; 32g Protein; 22g Carbohydrate

Cauliflower and Curry Soup

Gumbo Style Soup

1/2	pound chicken breast diced
1/3	pound sausage lean
1/2	pound shrimp fresh, peeled, deveined, chopped
6	cups chicken broth
2	cups scallions thinly sliced on an angle
2	cups green peppers diced
2	cups okra sliced
2	cups celery diced
2	teaspoons jalapeno minced
1	teaspoon garlic chopped
1	cup Walden Farms Tomato and Basil Sauce
1/2	tablespoon olive oil
1	bay leaf
1/2	teaspoon dried oregano
1/2	teaspoon onion powder
1/4	teaspoon dried thyme
1/4	teaspoon dried basil
1	teaspoon sea salt
1/2	teaspoon pepper freshly ground

Heat oil over medium-high heat in a large, heavy-bottomed soup pot. Add sausage. Sauté until it begins to become firm (about 1 minute), stirring occasionally. Add chicken and sauté until it loses its raw appearance (after about 2 to 3 minutes). Add pepper, celery, okra, scallions, jalapeno and garlic.

Add vegetables, stirring occasionally until tender. Add sauce and chicken broth. Add bay leaf, salt, pepper, oregano, onion powder, thyme and basil. Simmer for 30 minutes. Add shrimps. If liquid has reduced too much, and water. Do not allow the soup to return to a boil. Adjust the seasoning with salt and pepper, if necessary.

Per Serving: 437 Calories; 24g Fat; 36g Protein; 17g Carbohydrate

Minestrone Style Soup

1	pound prosciutto julienned
1	packet Ideal Protein Pancakes prepared, sliced fine
1	cup vegetable bouillon
2	cups celery stalk sliced
1	cup radish sliced
2	cups green pepper sliced
1	cup green onions sliced
1	cup leek white part only
2	cloves garlic crushed
1	tablespoon basil
1	bay leaf
2	cups Walden Farms Tomato and Basil Sauce
1	tablespoon sea salt
1	teaspoon pepper

Sauté garlic, green onions, celery and leek. Add green pepper. Add Tomato and Basil sauce and vegetable stock. Add 3 cups of water and bay leaf. Cook for 25 minutes. Add radish, prosciutto and cook for an additional 10 minutes. Adjust seasoning. Add pancakes and basil just before serving.

Per Serving: 361 Calories; 11g Fat; 40g Protein; 25g Carbohydrate

Egg Drop Soup

1 1/2	pounds	shrimp cooked
4	egg whites well beaten
4	packets Ideal Protein Chicken Soup prepared
4	cups Chinese cabbage sliced
4	cups green onions finely chopped
1/2	cup soy sauce
2	teaspoons curry paste
1	teaspoon Chinese 5-spice powder

Bring chicken soup to a boil in a large saucepan. Add soy sauce, 5-spice and 1 cup of water. Return to a boil. Add cabbage and simmer for 10 minutes. Remove from heat. Stir in green onions and shrimps.

Combine egg whites with curry paste. Return soup to a simmer and quickly stir in egg mixture, making circles with a spoon. Eggs will separate to form fine threads. Serve immediately.

Per Serving: 370 Calories; 5g Fat; 61g Protein; 17g Carbohydrate

Shrimp and Leek Soup

2	pounds shrimp fresh, peeled, deveined
4	cups fish stock
2	cups spinach finely chopped
4	cups leek finely chopped
2	cups green onions
1	tablespoon olive oil
1	teaspoon curry paste
	sea salt to taste
	pepper to taste

Sear shrimp in hot olive oil. Remove from heat and set 4 shrimps aside. Cut the rest into small pieces.

When oil is cooled, (just warm), add leek, green onions and curry paste. Cook slowly until leek is tender. Add fish stock. Simmer for 15 minutes. Add spinach and bring to a boil.

Season and add shrimp pieces.
Serve the soup and decorate with the whole shrimp.

Per Serving: 452 Calories; 14g Fat; 49g Protein; 22g Carbohydrate

Egg Drop Soup

Hearty Cod and Vegetable Soup

2	pounds cod cubed
2	cups cauliflower
2	cups zucchini diced
2	cups celery root diced
2	cups green onions finely chopped
2	tablespoons garlic minced
1	tablespoon basil crushed
6	ounces Walden Farms Fish Sauce
1	dash hot pepper sauce
1/4	cup olive oil
3/4	teaspoon sea salt

Slowly cook green onions in olive oil. Add zucchini and celery root. Add garlic, fish sauce and 1 cup of water. Add cauliflower florets and bring to a boil. Add hot sauce and salt.

When vegetables are cooked, add bite-sized fish. Let simmer until fish is tender. Adjust seasoning. Serve very hot.

Per Serving: 361 Calories; 15g Fat; 44g Protein; 12g Carbohydrate

Easy Tilapia Chowder

1 3/4	pounds tilapia
1	cup fish stock
2	cups fennel
2	cups celery diced
2	cups zucchini diced
2	cups green onions sliced
2	cups Walden Farms Tomato and Basil Sauce
2	cups Walden Farms Alfredo Sauce
2	tablespoons olive oil

Sauté celery and green onions in olive oil until golden. Add fennel and fish stock. Simmer for 20 minutes or until vegetables are tender.

Add sauces and zucchini. Cook for an additional 5 minutes (add water if too thick). Add tilapia and simmer for 5 more minutes until fish is cooked. Serve very hot.

Per Serving: 351 Calories; 13g Fat; 44g Protein; 11g Carbohydrate

Soups, salads and eggs

Hearty Cod and Vegetable Soup

Bouillabaisse

1	pound	halibut steaks
4		clams
2/3	cup	clam juice
1/4	pound	lobster meat fresh
1/4	pound	shrimp fresh, peeled, deveined
1/4	pound	crabmeat
2 1/2	cups	zucchini cut in fine strips
2	cups	celery chopped
1	cup	asparagus cut 1" thick
1/2	cup	radish sliced
1	cup	leek sliced
1	cup	green onions sliced
1	clove	garlic minced
1	teaspoon	parsley chopped
1	teaspoon	thyme
1/2	cup	Walden Farms Tomato and Basil Sauce
3	tablespoons	olive oil
1	teaspoon	paprika
1	teaspoon	onion powder
1	pinches	saffron
1	drop	hot pepper sauce
1	teaspoon	sea salt

NOTE: Retain all cooking water to be filtered and used as a base.

Sear halibut steaks in olive oil. Add shrimp. When cooked, set aside.
Cook lobster in boiling water for 6 minutes, remove meat from shell. Set meat aside with the halibut and the shrimp. Set cooking water aside.
Simmer lobster shells in clam juice for 30 minutes. Add 6 cups of lobster water to prepare a base.

Sauté celery, garlic and paprika in the halibut pan for 5 minutes. Do not allow to brown.
Add Tomato and Basil sauce and parsley. Cook for 4 minutes.
Cook asparagus in salted, boiling water. Set aside.

Sauté green onions, zucchini, radish and leek. Add asparagus. Add filtered base, saffron and thyme. Simmer for approximately 20 minutes. Add fish and reheat.
Serve very hot.

Per Serving: 380 Calories; 15g Fat; 45g Protein; 14g Carbohydrate

Soups, salads and eggs

Dungeness Crab Bisque

2	pounds crab shells
2	pounds crab meat
1	cup Ideal Protein Chicken Soup prepared
2	cups spirulina (or any type of seaweed)
2	cups celery root sliced
2	cups leek
2	cups fennel sliced
1	hot chili peppers finely chopped
1	cup Walden Farms Tomato and Basil Sauce
2	tablespoons olive oil

Warm 1 tablespoon of the olive oil in skillet. Add crab shells. When the shells are red, cover with water and simmer for 30 minutes. Remove meat from shells. Do not discard liquid.

In another pan, warm the other half of olive oil. Add celery, leek, chili pepper and fennel. Add chicken soup, shell cooking liquid and Tomato and Basil sauce. Cook slowly until vegetables are tender.

If the bisque is too liquid, reduce through simmering, then adjust the seasoning. Before serving, add crab meat and seaweed.

NOTE: For crispiness, you can fry the seaweed in olive oil.

Per Serving: 395 Calories; 11g Fat; 60g Protein; 16g Carbohydrate

Roasted Garlic Soup with Lobster

1 1/2	pounds	lobster meat, cooked
2	packets	Ideal Protein Pancakes prepared (4)
6	cups	chicken broth
2	cups	green onions
4	garlic	roasted
1	teaspoon	jalapeño chopped
2	tablespoons	Walden Farms Blue Cheese Dip
1	tablespoon	olive oil

Cut top of garlic bulb. Brush with olive oil. Bake in 375 degree oven for about 30 minutes or until clove is tender. Separate clove from skin. Purée cloves.
Add garlic skin to beef broth in a large saucepan. Cover and simmer for 15 minutes. Remove garlic skin. Add jalapeño and half of the garlic purée to broth and re-heat to serving temperature. Add lobster meat just before serving and bring to a boil.

Toast prepared pancakes under broiler on one side. Remove and spread untoasted side with olive oil.

Spread the rest of garlic purée and cheese dip over pancake. Broil for approximately 30 seconds. Place a pancake in each of four soup bowls before pouring in soup.

Per Serving: 401 Calories, 7g Fat; 55g Protein; 27g Carbohydrate

---

Ranch Salad with Smoked and Ground Beef

1	pound	ground beef, extra lean	1/2	cup	cucumber seeded and diced
1/2	pound	smoked chipped beef	1/2	cup	green onion sliced
6	cups	iceberg lettuce shredded			Walden Farms Chipotle Ranch Dressing
1	cup	green peppers diced	1	teaspoon	chili powder

In a skillet, sauté ground beef on medium heat. Drain excess fat.
Sprinkle with chili and continue cooking until meat is done. Remove from pan and let cool.
Mix lettuce with green onions and peppers. Garnish with ground beef, smoked beef and cucumber. Drizzle with dressing.

Per Serving: 368 Calories; 22g Fat; 34g Protein; 7g Carbohydrate

Soybeans Sprouts in Garlic Salad

1/2	pound shrimp cooked	2	teaspoons Walden Farms
1/2	pound crab meat cooked		Fruit Spread chopped
7	cups soybeans sprouts	5	tablespoons soy sauce
4	tablespoons garlic	2	tablespoons sesame oil
4	tablespoons green onions	6	tablespoons cider vinegar
	trimmed & minced	2	tablespoons sesame seeds
3	tablespoons fresh ginger		
	chopped fine		

Toast the sesame seeds in a baking pan for 5 minutes, stirring often, until they are golden. Place the bean sprouts in a large heat-resistant bowl and set it aside.

In a medium size skillet over moderately low heat, cook the garlic, green onions and ginger in oil for 2 to 3 minutes, until green onionsare limp. Add all the remaining ingredients to the skillet and increase the heat to bring the mixture to a boil. Keep uncovered, for 1 minute to slightly reduce the liquid.

Pour the dressing over the bean sprouts, toss well and cover the bowl. Chill the salad for several hours. Toss again before serving. Top with shrimp, crab and sesame seeds.

Per Serving: 384 Calories; 19g Fat; 42g Protein; 20g Carbohydrate

Celery Root Salad with Smoked Beef

2	pounds smoked chipped beef	4	tablespoons Walden Farms
7	cups celery root grated		Mayonnaise
1/2	cup celery leaves	1	tablespoon Dijon mustard
1/2	cup radish slices	1	teaspoon lemon juice

Combine celery root with mustard, lemon juice and mayonnaise. Refrigerate for at least 2 hours. To plate, decorate the salad mixture with radish slices and celery leaves and surround with beef.

NOTE: You can use fresh jalapeños in this salad.

Per Serving: 354 Calories; 10g Fat; 48g Protein; 13g Carbohydrate

Soybeans Sprouts in Garlic Salad

Coleslaw Salad

2	pounds cooked or smoked ham, extra lean sliced
6	cups cabbage chopped fine
2	cups green peppers chopped fine
2	tablespoons Walden Farms Coleslaw Dressing
1	teaspoon hot chili powder
1/4	teaspoon sea salt
1/8	teaspoon pepper

Combine green peppers with dressing, hot chili powder, salt and pepper. Mix well. Add cabbage, mix again and refrigerate for at least 2 hours before serving.
Serve topped with ham slices.

Per Serving: 353 Calories; 12g Fat; 47g Protein; 15g Carbohydrate

Zucchini and Prosciutto Salad

1 1/4	pounds prosciutto sliced 1/2" thick	2	teaspoons parsley chopped
2	cups zucchini sliced 1/4" thick	1	tablespoon olive oil
2	cups lettuce leaves	3	tablespoons cider vinegar
2	cups green peppers roasted		curry powder to taste
2	cups green onions chopped		sea salt to taste
2	cloves garlic sliced		pepper to taste

Sauté zucchini and green onions in olive oil for a few minutes. Season.
Cut roasted pepper into 2" pieces.

In a bowl, mix vinegar, oil, garlic, parsley, curry, salt and pepper. Add vegetables.
Set aside for 30 minutes.

Mix half of the prosciutto with the salad.
Serve salad on lettuce leaves. Top with the other half of prosciutto.

> **NOTE: The prosciutto you will use to top the salad can be dried in the oven until crispy.**

Per Serving: 358 Calories; 16g Fat; 42g Protein; 12g Carbohydrate

Coleslaw Salad

Grilled Mushroom and Celery Heart Salad

4	cups portobello mushroom (caps) stems removed	1/4	cup basil leaves	
1 1/4	pounds smoked chopped beef	2	tablespoons Walden Farms Mayonnaise	
1	cup greens	1/4	cup olive oil	
2	cups celery hearts thinly sliced	1	teaspoon sea salt	
3	pieces lemons zested and juiced	1/2	teaspoon pepper	
1/4	cup parsley			

Preheat grill to HIGH.
In a bowl, toss mushrooms with 1 teaspoon of olive oil.
In blender, combine the rest of olive oil, lemon juice, lemon zest, basil, mayonnaise, salt and pepper until smooth. Set aside.

Place mushrooms, cap side down on grill. Grill until golden and slightly charred (4 to 5 minutes). Turn. Remove.

When cool enough to handle, cut into 1/8" thick slices.
In a bowl, toss greens, celery, parsley and mushrooms and beef with half of the dressing. Transfer to serving plate. Drizzle with remaining dressing.

Per Serving: 380 Calories; 21g Fat; 34g Protein; 19g Carbohydrate

....

Greek Mushroom Salad

2	pounds calamari	2	tablespoons Walden Farms French Onion Dip
6	ounces anchovies		
3	cups mixed salad greens	1	tablespoon olive oil
3	cups oyster mushrooms thinly sliced		ground coriander to taste
2	cups button mushrooms thinly sliced		sea salt to taste
1/4	cup Walden Farms Jersey Salad Dressing		pepper to taste

Quickly cook calamari in 1 tablespoon of olive oil. Season with salt, pepper and coriander. Remove calamari from pan and sauté mushrooms until tender. Add dressing. Refrigerate for 1 hour.

Place mushrooms on a bed of mixed greens and top with anchovies and calamari.

Per Serving: 363 Calories; 11g Fat; 51g Protein; 13g Carbohydrate

Soups, salads and eggs

Thai Style Fennel Salad

1	pound	beef tenderloin, lean
1	package	Ideal Protein Pancakes sliced into thin strips
5	cups	fennel
2	cups	radish thinly sliced and halved
2	cloves	garlic minced
1		jalapeño chopped
1	tablespoon	fresh ginger chopped
3	tablespoons	olive oil divided
2	tablespoons	cider vinegar
1/2	teaspoon	red pepper flakes
2	tablespoons	soy sauce
1	tablespoon	mint leaves (optional)

Partially freeze steak. Slice across the grain into 1/4-inch strips. Place in large bowl.

Combine 2 tablespoons of oil, vinegar, soy sauce, half of the jalapeño, garlic, fresh ginger and pepper flakes in small bowl. Pour mixture over beef. Marinate for 1 hour.

Bake prepared pancakes in oven until crispy.

Drain beef.

Heat remaining 1 tablespoon of oil in large skillet over medium-high heat. Add beef and remaining jalapeño. Cook 3 to 5 minutes or until no longer pink, drain fat and set beef aside.

Add marinade to pan and boil for 3 minutes. Reduce by half.
Combine beef, liquid from skillet, vegetables and pancakes in large bowl. Toss to coat. Sprinkle with mint, if desired.

NOTE: Partially freezing the steak makes it easier to thinly slice the meat.

Per Serving: 352 Calories; 19g Fat; 31g Protein; 16g Carbohydrate

Roast Beef Salad

1 1/4	pounds beef tenderloin, lean cooked, cut into strips	3	tablespoons olive oil
4	cups greens	8	tablespoons cider vinegar
2	cups green pepper cut into strips		Tabasco sauce to taste
2	cups celery stalk sliced 1/4" thick		sea salt to taste
2	tablespoons fresh parsley chopped fine		pepper to taste
2	tablespoons fresh basil chopped fine		

Mix vegetables in a large bowl.
Mix vinegar with salt, pepper and hot sauce. Add oil. Pour over vegetables. Mix well and refrigerate for 30 minutes.

Serve on a bed of lettuce and garnish with slices of roast beef and fresh herbs.

Per Serving: 354 Calories; 20g Fat; 33g Protein; 12g Carbohydrate

....

Spinach Salad with Ham

3/4	pound ham slices
8	hard-boiled eggs sliced 1/4" thick
2	cups green onions diced fine
6	cups fresh spinach chopped
2	tablespoon olive oil
1/4	cup cider vinegar
1/4	teaspoon sea salt
1/8	teaspoon pepper

Cook ham on medium heat in 1 teaspoon of oil until crispy. Keep only 1/2 teaspoon of drippings. Add green onions to the pan and sauté for a few minutes. Remove from pan and mix with ham.

DRESSING: Add vinegar to the pan and reduce. Add olive oil, salt and pepper.

TO PLATE: Arrange spinach leaves, top with ham and green onions. Garnish with egg slices and drizzle with dressing.

Per Serving: 353 Calories; 21g Fat; 32g Protein; 9g Carbohydrate

Roast Beef Salad

Turkey Cabbage Salad

1 1/4	pounds turkey breast cooked		1/4	teaspoon Tabasco sauce (optional)	
6	cups shredded cabbage finely shredded		3	tablespoons olive oil	
1 1/2	cups onion finely shredded		3	tablespoons cider vinegar	
1/2	cup red onion sliced fine		1	tablespoon Dijon mustard	
3	tablespoons parsley chopped		1/2	teaspoon dried basil crumbled	
1	clove garlic minced				

In large bowl, combine all ingredients except cabbage, onions and turkey. Mix well. Add cabbage and onions. Toss well to coat with dressing. Arrange on a plate. Top with slices of cooked turkey. Decorate with red onion slices.
Serve with additional Tabasco if desired.

Per Serving: 354 Calories; 20g Fat; 31g Protein; 14g Carbohydrate

Smoked Turkey with Leek and Citrus Salad

1	pound smoked turkey breast		2	teaspoons Walden Farms Orange Spread chopped	
4	cups chicken broth		2	tablespoons olive oil	
6	cups leek white part			sea salt to taste	
2	cups radicchio sliced			pepper to taste	
2	lemons zested				
2	tablespoons lime juice				

Clean outside part of the leek. In a pot, place leek with chicken stock and seasoning. Add lemon zests. Bring to boil and simmer until leek is tender.

FOR DRESSING:
In another pot, take 1 cup of stock and reduce to 2 tablespoon. Add orange spread, lime juice and olive oil. Adjust seasoning.
Mix radicchio with dressing and arrange in the middle of plates. Surround with leek and slices of smoked turkey.

> NOTE: When chicken broth is reduced, taste for seasoning. It may already be salty enough.

Per Serving: 389 Calories; 16g Fat; 37g Protein; 24g Carbohydrate

Warm Chicken Salad
with Fruit Dressing

1 1/2	pounds	chicken breast cooked and shredded
1	packet	Ideal Protein Pancakes prepared
4	cups	romaine lettuce chopped
3	cups	endives chopped
1	cup	green onions
3	cloves	garlic chopped fine
4	tablespoons	lemon juice to taste
1	tablespoon	fresh basil chopped fine
1	tablespoon	fresh parsley chopped fine
1	teaspoon	Walden Farms Fruit Spread chopped
2	tablespoons	olive oil
1	tablespoon	cider vinegar
		sea salt to taste
		pepper to taste

Arrange lettuce in a serving bowl.

In a skillet over medium heat, temperature 1 tablespoons of oil. Add garlic, green onions and chicken. Season and cook on high heat for 2 minutes. Add fruit spread, vinegar and mix well. Cook on low heat for 1 minute.

Cut prepared Pancakes into squares. Sprinkle with fresh herbs, salt and pepper to taste. Drizzle with lemon juice.

Per Serving: 353 Calories; 20g Fat; 34g Protein; 9g Carbohydrate

Crab Salad

2	pounds crab meat cooked		2	cups Walden Farms Mayonnaise
4	cups cucumber diced		2	tablespoons olive oil
4	cups asparagus		1	tablespoon onion powder
1/2	cup capers		2	teaspoons sea salt
1/2	cup lemon juice		1/2	teaspoon pepper
1/2	cup parsley finely chopped			

Mix crab with onion powder, capers and cucumber. Add Mayonnaise and refrigerate for at least 3 hours.

Cook asparagus in salted, boiling water. Let cool.
Place asparagus on plate, drizzle with olive oil. Top with crab mixture and garnish with parsley.

Per Serving: 360 Calories; 10g Fat; 51g Protein; 13g Carbohydrate

....

Calamari Salad on Garden Greens

2 1/4	pounds calamari sliced
3	cups greens
2	cups green peppers roasted and diced
1	cup celery stalks finely chopped
2	cups green onions thinly sliced
1/2	cup fresh basil finely chopped
3/4	cup Walden Farms Zesty Italian Dressing
4	tablespoons Walden Farms Honey Dijon Dressing
2	tablespoons olive oil
1	tablespoon cider vinegar
	sea salt to taste
	pepper to taste

In a large bowl, combine green onions, peppers, salad greens, basil and celery.
Mix well. In another bowl, mix dressings and vinegar.

In hot oil, sauté the calamari on high for only a few minutes.
To plate, make a bed with the vegetables, top with calamari, add the dressing and serve.

Per Serving: 357 Calories; 11g Fat; 43g Protein; 20g Carbohydrate

Crab Salad

Happy Seafood Salad

3/4	pound	shrimp fresh, peeled, deveined
3/4	pound	scallops
1/2	pound	crab meat
1/4	cup	seaweed
3/4	cup	alfalfa sprouts
2	cups	endives
3	cups	spinach
2	cups	radicchio
1	teaspoon	chervil

2	teaspoons	Walden Farms Orange Spread chopped
4	tablespoons	olive oil
1	tablespoon	cider vinegar
1	teaspoon	curry powder
		sea salt to taste
		pepper to taste

Mix cider vinegar and curry powder. Allow scallops to sit in mixture for 5 minutes.

NOTE: If preferred, you may sauté Scallops 2 minutes in a pan instead of vinegar method.

Arrange salad on plates.

Prepare vinaigrette using curry, vinegar, chervil and orange spread. Mix with olive oil. Salt and pepper. Coat shrimp and scallops with vinaigrette. Drizzle the rest on salad leaves. Top salad with seafood.

Cut seaweed in fine strips. Quickly sauté in olive oil until crispy. Sprinkle over salad.

Per Serving: 357 Calories; 16g Fat; 44g Protein; 6g Carbohydrate

....

Lobster on a Bed of Salad

3/4	pound	lobster meat, cooked
8		eggs
1	packet	Ideal Protein Pancakes prepared (2) cut in strips
3	cups	greens
3	cups	asparagus cooked
2	cups	radicchio
1	teaspoon	ginger crushed

2	tablespoons	Walden Farms Balsamic Dressing •
2	tablespoons	olive oil
1	tablespoon	cider vinegar
		sea salt to taste
		pepper to taste

Sauté eggs with olive oil.
Once prepared, toast pancakes in oven until crispy.
Marinade lobster in olive oil with ginger and vinegar.
Mix greens, asparagus and radicchio. Prepare a bed on each plate. Drizzle with dressing.
Top with eggs. Garnish with shrimps and pancake crips.

Per Serving: 367 Calories; 18g Fat; 38g Protein; 13g Carbohydrate

Happy Seafood Salad

Mussel Salad with Basil

2 1/2	pounds mussels washed and drained		1	tablespoon olive oil
1/2	pound shrimp cooked		1/2	tablespoon cider vinegar
2	cups lettuce leaves		1	teaspoon saffron optional
2	cups radicchio leaves			sea salt to taste
2	cups endive separated into leaves			pepper to taste
2	cups green onions finely chopped			
1	tablespoon basil finely chopped			
3 1/2	ounces Walden Farms Creamy Italian Dressing			

Cook mussels in a covered pan with green onions, 1/2 cup water, cider vinegar, olive oil and saffron. Stir often until mussels are fully opened. Drain and transfer to a bowl.
Reserve 4 tablespoons of the cooking liquid.
Let cool. Remove from shells.

Prepare sauce: Mix dressing with cooking liquid until creamy. Add basil and pepper.
Pour over mussels and mix. Add shrimp.

Cut salad into strips. Arrange salad on small plates or in glass cups and top with mussels. Decorate with basil leaves.

Per Serving: 388 Calories; 11g Fat; 48g Protein; 22g Carbohydrate

Zesty Shrimp and Crab Salad

1 1/4	pounds crab meat cooked		2	tablespoons Walden Farms Alfredo Sauce
1 1/4	pounds shrimp cooked		2	tablespoons Walden Farms Seafood Sauce
3	cups celery chopped fine			
2	cups greens		2	tablespoons Walden Farms Mayonnaise
2	cups cucumber chopped fine			
1	cup green peppers chopped		1	tablespoon olive oil
3	tablespoons lemon juice			
1	teaspoon dill weed			

Mix all vegetables, shrimp, crab with sauces and olive oil.
Arrange greens in the bottom of a bowl. Top with crab and shrimp. Sprinkle with dill.

Per Serving: 363 Calories; 8g Fat; 60g Protein; 11g Carbohydrate

Mussel Salad with Basil

Shrimp Salad with Soybean Sprouts

2	pounds shrimp fresh, peeled, deveined		1	tablespoon white vinegar
2	cups oyster mushrooms		2	teaspoons Tamarind Sauce
2	cups red peppers cut 1/4" thick		1/2	teaspoon hot chili powder
4	cups soybean sprouts			coriander to taste
1	teaspoon chives finely chopped			sea salt to taste
1	teaspoon sesame oil			pepper to taste

Sauté peppers in sesame oil. Add mushrooms. Let cool.
Cook shrimp in salted water (enough to cover) with 1/2 of the Tamarind sauce for
1 to 2 minutes. Drain and let cool.

Place soybean sprouts in boiling water and remove as soon as the water returns to a boil.
Rinse in cold water and drain. Dry in paper towels.
Prepare the sauce by mixing chili powder, vinegar, remaining Tamarind sauce and
sesame oil. Combine sprouts, red peppers, mushrooms and chives. To plate, arrange
vegetables, surround with shrimp and sprinkle with coriander.

NOTE: You can use raw soybean sprouts instead of cooking them.

Per Serving: 384 Calories; 10g Fat; 57g Protein; 19g Carbohydrate

....

Quail and Shrimp Fiesta Salad

8	quail breasts, skinless		2	tablespoon lemon juice
8	quail eggs		1/4	cup coriander finely chopped
1/4	pound shrimp cooked		1	tablespoon olive oil
2	cups zucchini cubed		3	tablespoons salad oil
4	cups lettuce		1/2	teaspoon sea salt
2	cups green onions thinly sliced		1	dash pepper ground cumin
1/3	cup chili pepper finely chopped			

Hard boil quail eggs in boiling water for 5 minutes.
Sauté quail breasts in olive oil for about 7 minutes. Add zucchini. Set aside.
In a large bowl, combine lemon juice, oil, salt pepper and cumin. Add zucchini and mix
until combined. Chill for 30 minutes. Add green onions, chili pepper and half of the quail
eggs. To serve, arrange lettuce leaves on salad plates. Top with zucchini mix. Garnish
with quail breasts, shrimp and a sprig of coriander.

Per Serving: 357 Calories; 20g Fat; 36g Protein; 9g Carbohydrate

Soups, salads and eggs

Shrimp Salad with Soybean Sprouts

Caesar Egg Salad

4	eggs
8	egg whites
1	pound ham thin slices
24	romaine lettuce leaves
4	green pepper julienned
2	tablespoons parsley chopped fine
6	tablespoons Walden Farms Caesar Dressing
1	tablespoon olive oil

Wisk all egg, add seasoning, parsley and green peppers. Bake in oiled cake pan in a 350-degree oven until set. Cut into squares.
Sauté ham until crisp.

Mix romaine lettuce with Caesar dressing. Arrange on plate. Serve with a squares of egg and top with ham.

Per Serving: 357 Calories; 17g Fat; 39g Protein; 12g Carbohydrate

....

Egg and Smoked Haddock Salad

1 1/2	pounds smoked haddock julienned	2	tablespoons Walden Farms Mayonnaise
8	eggs hard boiled and quartered	2	teaspoons Dijon mustard to taste
4	cups lettuce leaves		garlic powder to taste
2	cups endive sliced		hot pepper sauce to taste
1	cup radicchio		sea salt to taste
1	cup green onions chopped fine		
4	tablespoons Walden Farms Dressing		

In a bowl, combine eggs, smoked haddock, mayonnaise, green onions, mustard and seasonings.

In a separate bowl, mix radicchio and endives with dressing.
Arrange a bed of lettuce on each plate. Top with endive and radicchio dressing and egg and Haddock mixture.

> **NOTE: Any smoked white fish will do. If not available, you can flavor marinated fish with smoked spices, such as smoked paprika.**

Per Serving: 375 Calories; 13g Fat; 57g Protein; 5g Carbohydrate

Caesar Egg Salad

Deviled Eggs with a Smoky Salad

1/2	pound	smoked chipped beef
1/2	pound	smoked turkey breast
8	eggs	hard-boiled
6	cups	lettuce leaves
2	cups	green pepper chopped fine
2	cups	Walden Farms Dijon Dressing
1/4	cup	Walden Farms Mayonnaise
2	cups	Walden Farms BBQ Sauce
2	tablespoons	Dijon mustard or to taste
		sea salt to taste
		pepper to taste

Slice hard boiled eggs in half. Carefully remove yolks without breaking the egg whites. Blend yolks with mayonnaise, green peppers, mustard, salt and pepper until smooth. Fill egg white halves with this mixture.

Cut salad leaves in big pieces and top with dressing. Add a bed top with the chipped meat and surround with deviled eggs.

Per Serving: 357 Calories; 17g Fat; 41g Protein; 9g Carbohydrate

....

Egg Foo Yung

1 1/2	pounds	crab meat cooked
16	egg whites	wisked
6	cups	soybean sprouts blanched
2	cups	green onions minced
4	tablespoons	Walden Farms Seafood Sauce
2	teaspoons	soy sauce
1	teaspoon	sea salt
1/2	teaspoon	pepper

Blanch soybean sprouts in a few tablespoons of salted, boiling water.
Beat egg whites well. Add drained bean sprouts, onion, salt and pepper and crab meat.
In a heated frying pan divide mixture into 4 and cook (as you would a pancake) in a small amount of oil.

Pour in the Seafood sauce and soy sauce. Cook until thickened.
Top pancakes with sauce and serve.

Per Serving: 381 Calories; 9g Fat; 64g Protein; 15g Carbohydrate

Soups, salads and eggs

Deviled Eggs with a Smoky Salad

Egg Salad with Sauté and Marinated Scallops

1 1/2	pounds scallops		1	tablespoon Walden Farms Mayonnaise
8	eggs hard-boiled chopped		2	tablespoons Walden Farms Chipotle Dressing
4	cups green peppers sliced thin		1	tablespoon olive oil
2	cups lettuce		1	tablespoon curry powder
2	cups radicchio			chili powder to taste
2	lemons			sea salt to taste
1/4	cup coriander chopped fine			
1	teaspoon habanera chili pepper chopped			

Marinate the scallops with lemon juice and curry powder for 30 minutes in the fridge.
Sauté the scallops in olive oil. Add 1/2 tablespoon of dressing.
In a bowl, mix eggs with mayonnaise and half of the coriander.

To plate: Arrange egg mixture in the center of plate. Place scallops around the mixture and decorate with coriander.
Add lettuce and raw green peppers on the side and drizzle with remaining dressing.

Per Serving: 391 Calories; 16g Fat; 43g Protein; 20g Carbohydrate

Scrambled Eggs with Asparagus

3/4	pound prosciutto julienned
8	eggs
8	cups asparagus
1	tablespoon Walden Farms Alfredo Sauce
1	teaspoon olive oil
	sea salt to taste
	pepper to taste

Mix eggs with prosciutto. Salt and pepper.
Blanch asparagus in salted, boiling water. Keep warm.
Put olive oil in cold pan. Add eggs. Slowly warm egg mixture, stirring constantly.
When cooked as desired, add Alfredo sauce.
Serve with asparagus on the side.

Per Serving: 385 Calories; 19g Fat; 42g Protein; 13g Carbohydrate

Soups, salads and eggs

Egg Salad with Sauté and
Marinated Scallops

Benedict Style Eggs

8	eggs	8	tablespoons Walden Farms Alfredo Sauce
1/2	pound smoked ham sliced		
2	packets Ideal Protein Pancakes (4) prepared	2	teaspoons olive oil
		1	teaspoon cider vinegar
4	cups lettuce greens		sea salt to taste
4	cups spinach		pepper to taste
4	tablespoons Walden Farms Dressing (your choice)		

Mix Alfredo sauce with 4 eggs.
Sauté smoked ham in 1 teaspoon of olive oil, add spinach.
In a medium size pot, simmer water with vinegar. Crack remaining 4 eggs and delicately pour into simmering water. Carefully turn with a spoon until cooked (approximately 5 minutes).
On each pancake, place a slice of smoked ham, spinach then a poached egg. Coat each with 2 tablespoons of the Alfredo Sauce mix and place under the broiler until eggs settle.

NOTE: If you prefer a more "fluffy" pancakes, add baking powder to the mix.

Per Serving: 358 Calories; 17g Fat; 36g Protein; 12g Carbohydrate

Lamb with Rosemary and Blue Cheese Scrambled Eggs

1 ½	pounds lamb chop lean cooked, cut into 1" cubes	1	tablespoon Walden Farms Blue Cheese Dip
2	egg whites	2	teaspoons olive oil
8	cups oyster mushrooms		sea salt to taste
2	cloves garlic crushed		pepper to taste
1	tablespoon rosemary chopped fine		

Whisk egg whites with rosemary and garlic. Add cooked lamb cubes.
Heat non-stick pan on medium-high temperature. Add olive oil. Remix the eggs and pour into pan. Cook eggs until creamy. Add dip and stir until blended.

In another pan, sauté oyster mushrooms until golden. Add sea salt.
Serve with scrambled eggs.

NOTE: The delicate taste of rosemary and blue cheese in the scrambled eggs is a true delight.

Per Serving: 359 Calories; 8g Fat; 43g Protein; 12g Carbohydrate

Benedict Style Eggs

Poached Eggs on a Nest of Vegetables

8	eggs		1	cup green peppers cut 1/4" thick
3/4	pound prosciutto sliced		1	cup zucchini cut 1/4" thick
1/2	packet Ideal Protein Salt and Vinegar Ridges crushed		3/4	cup Walden Farms Tomato and Basil Sauce
2	cups broccoli chopped		1	tablespoon onion powder
2	cups spinach chopped		1/4	teaspoon pepper
2	cups mushrooms chopped			

Sauté mushrooms until they are golden brown. Add spinach. Cook until vegetables are tender. Blanche broccoli in salted, boiling water. Add peppers. Add to the spinach mixture. Add Tomato and Basil sauce and season. Poach eggs in the cooking water from the broccoli.
Bake prosciutto slices in a 250-degree oven until crispy (around 10 minutes).

TO PLATE: Prepare 4 portions of vegetable on warmed plates. With the back of a spoon, make a nest in the vegetables. Top each "nest" with a poached egg. Sprinkle with crumbled ridges. Broil for a few minutes.
Garnish with prosciutto.

Per Serving: 376 Calories; 18g Fat; 41g Protein; 11g Carbohydrate

Eggs Cocotte with Asparagus Puree

1/2	pound ham cubed		4	cups asparagus
8	eggs		4	tablespoons Walden Farms Alfredo Sauce
2	packets Ideal Protein Pancakes prepared (4 sliced thin)			sea salt to taste
4	cups cauliflower			pepper to taste

Oil 4 small oven-safe dishes (ramekins). Add smoked ham, salt and pepper to each and break 1 egg in each.
Cook in double boiler on stove. Water should simmer not boil.
Cook cauliflower in salted, boiling water. Purée with Alfredo sauce. Set aside.
Cook asparagus in salted, boiling water. Set aside.
Spread cauliflower purée on the white part of cooked eggs.
Serve asparagus on the side with slices of pancakes.

Per Serving: 377 Calories; 17g Fat; 37g Protein; 20g Carbohydrate

Poached Eggs with Shrimp

1 1/2   pounds shrimp fresh, peeled, deveined
8   eggs
8   cups spinach
1/2   cup Walden Farms Tomato and Basil Sauce
1   tablespoon olive oil
1   teaspoon cider vinegar
         sea salt to taste
         pepper to taste

Sauté shrimp in olive oil. Add Tomato and Basil sauce and simmer for 5 minutes.
Add vinegar to simmering water. Poach eggs for 5 minutes. Sauté spinach in olive oil salt and pepper.

In a gratin dish, make a nest of spinach. Place eggs in the center. Coat with Tomato and Basil sauce. Broil for 2 minutes.
Plate and add shrimp on the side.

Per Serving: 372 Calories; 16g Fat; 49g Protein; 4g Carbohydrate

....

Eggs Creole

1 1/2   pounds shrimp cooked
1/2   packet Ideal Protein Salt and Vinegar Ridges crushed
2   egg whites
4   cups green peppers chopped
4   cups green onions chopped
2   cups Walden Farms Tomato and Basil Sauce
1   tablespoon olive oil
1   teaspoon hot sauce

Cook green peppers and green onions in olive oil. Once cooled, add egg whites and salt and pepper. Pour mixture into oiled oven dish. Put in a double broiler and cook slowly until the egg whites are set.
Cut the cooked eggs to the desired shape with a knife or a cookie cutter.
Warm Tomato and Basil sauce with hot sauce.

In a separate oiled baking dish, put a layer of sauce and with cooked eggs and shrimp.
Coat with more sauce and sprinkle with Ridges.
Bake at 350 degrees for 20 minutes or until Ridges are brown.

Per Serving: 386 Calories; 7g Fat; 57g Protein; 22g Carbohydrate

Egg Ratatouille Pie

3/4	pound prosciutto cut into 1" pieces	1	teaspoon dried basil
16	egg whites beaten	1	teaspoon dried thyme
3	cups zucchini chopped	3/4	teaspoon sea salt
2	cups green pepper chopped	1/4	teaspoon pepper
2	cups green onions chopped		
2	cloves garlic crushed	PESTO SAUCE	
1	cup Walden Farms Tomato and Basil Sauce	1/2	cup basil leaves
		1	teaspoon olive oil
2	tablespoons olive oil	1	teaspoon garlic crushed

Heat oven to 400 degrees. Lightly grease a 10x1 1/2" pie plate.
Cook zucchini, pepper and garlic in olive oil in 10" skillet over medium heat, stirring occasionally until vegetables are crisp and tender (5 to 10 minutes).
Spread vegetables and seasoning in pie plate and top with prosciutto and green onions.

PESTO SAUCE: Wash and dry basil. Remove stems. Blend with garlic, salt and add olive oil.
Beat egg whites with pesto until smooth. Pour into pie plate. Bake until knife inserted halfway between center and edge comes out clean, after 30 to 35 minutes.
Let stand 5 minutes before cutting.
Serve with warmed Tomato and Basil sauce.

Per Serving: 379 Calories; 16g Fat; 42g Protein; 19g Carbohydrate

Vegetable and Shrimp Frittata

1 1/2	pounds shrimp cooked	1	tablespoon olive oil
16	egg whites beaten	1	tablespoon curry paste
3	cups green peppers cut 1" thick		sea salt to taste
2 1/2	cups green onions sliced		pepper to taste
2 1/2	cups leek sliced		

Slowly cook green onions and leek in olive oil. Season. Add shrimp and curry paste.
Let cool.

Beat eggs and add to vegetables. Pour into oiled oven dish and bake in a 350-degree oven until eggs are set.

Per Serving: 381 Calories; 9g Fat; 52g Protein; 23g Carbohydrate

Egg Ratatouille Pie

Broccoli Frittata

4	eggs	2	tablespoons olive oil
8	egg whites	1	teaspoon dried basil
1/2	pound ham	1/2	teaspoon sea salt
7	cups cooked broccoli chopped	1/4	teaspoon pepper
1	cup parsley chopped fine		

Blanch broccoli in salted, boiling water. Cool. Chop.
In a large bowl, beat all eggs, add parsley, basil, salt and pepper until just blended. Stir in broccoli, ham and parsley.

Heat oil in a 10" ovenproof skillet over medium heat. Pour in egg mixture. Cook over low to medium heat until eggs are almost set but still moist on the surface about 10 to 15 minutes.

Cut into wedges to serve.

NOTE: Frittata may be served hot, warm or cold.

Per Serving: 353 Calories; 19g Fat; 32g Protein; 18g Carbohydrate

Turkey Frittata

1 1/2	pounds turkey breast cooked and shredded	2	tablespoons lemon juice
16	egg whites whisked	2	teaspoons olive oil
4	cups mushrooms sliced	1	tablespoon onion powder
4	cups frozen spinach drained	1	teaspoon curry paste
1	clove garlic minced	1/8	teaspoon pepper

Sauté mushrooms and garlic in oil for 5 minutes. Add onion powder, spinach, lemon juice and pepper. Cook on low heat for 3 minutes. Let cool.

Add the turkey, eggs and curry paste to the spinach mixture. Pour into a round, oiled baking dish. Bake in a 350-degree oven until eggs are set. Cut into wedges and serve. Drizzle with lemon juice.

Per Serving: 388 Calories; 14g Fat; 52g Protein; 13g Carbohydrate

Broccoli Frittata

Quiche

1/2	pound ham diced
2	packets Ideal Protein Pancakes prepared (4)
8	eggs
4	cups spinach
2	cups green onions
2	cups asparagus
4	tablespoons Walden Farms Alfredo Sauce

Line an oiled pie mold with prepared pancakes (for pie shell). Bake in a 375-degree oven for 5 minutes.

Sauté spinach, green onions and asparagus. Add ham. Put well drained vegetables & ham mixture in pie shell.

Beat eggs with Alfredo sauce. Pour in pie shell.
Cook 15 minutes or until eggs are set.

> **NOTE: Allow to cool for a few minutes before serving.**

Per Serving: 359 Calories; 17g Fat; 35g Protein; 17g Carbohydrate

....

Mushroom Omelets

8	eggs
1 1/2	egg whites
6	cups portobello mushrooms
2	cups green onions
1	teaspoon olive oil
	sea salt to taste
	pepper to taste

Sauté mushrooms and green onions.
Beat eggs and egg white. Salt and pepper.
Heat olive oil in hot pan. Add egg mixture and stir for 1 minute. Let omelette set. Top center with mushrooms. Fold in half and serve.

Per Serving: 353 Calories; 13g Fat; 39g Protein; 22g Carbohydrate

Soups, salads and eggs

Quiche

Asparagus and Curry Egg Casserole

24	egg whites		1	teaspoon white vinegar
3/4	pound ham cooked and cubed		4	teaspoons curry paste
8	cups asparagus			sea salt to taste
1/2	teaspoon minced garlic			pepper to taste
1	teaspoon olive oil			

Cook asparagus in salted, boiling water until tender.
Lightly mix egg whites with curry paste and seasoning. Pour into oiled casserole dish with cubed ham. Place in bain-marie, in a 375-degree oven for 10 minutes or until egg whites are set.

Place asparagus in an oven-safe dish. Baste with olive oil and garlic. Salt and pepper. Bake for 5 minutes or until hot.

TO PLATE: Top eggs with asparagus.

> **NOTE: A Bain Marie is a cooking container holding hot water, into which a pan is placed for slow cooking. Usually used in the oven.**

Per Serving: 355 Calories; 13g Fat; 42g Protein; 18g Carbohydrate

---

Spanish Omelette

8	eggs
1/2	pound prosciutto julienned
4	cups green peppers
4	cups green onions
1	teaspoon garlic crushed
1	tablespoon Walden Farms Tomato and Basil Sauce
2	teaspoons olive oil

Cook green peppers and green onions in 1 teaspoon of olive oil. Add garlic. Season. Let cool.

Beat eggs and combine with Tomato and Basil sauce and add cold vegetables.
In a skillet, warm remaining olive oil. Add egg mixture and prosciutto. Cook on medium temperature for 5 minutes. Finish in a 375-degree oven until eggs are set.

Per Serving: 350 Calories; 17g Fat; 31g Protein; 18g Carbohydrate

Asparagus and Curry
Egg Casserole

Grilled Vegetable Platter with Turkey

1 1/2	pounds	turkey breast
2	cups	zucchini sliced 1/2" thick
4	cups	green peppers sliced 1/2" thick
2	cups	mushrooms
1	cup	Walden Farms Balsamic Dressing
2	tablespoons	olive oil
		sea salt to taste
		pepper to taste
		Skewers prepared

In large resealable plastic bag, combine all ingredients (except turkey and olive oil) and marinate in refrigerator for 30 minutes or overnight.

Either thread vegetables onto skewers or place in grill basket and cook until tender. Season and brush the turkey breast with olive oil and grill.

Slice the turkey, and arrange on the grilled vegetables.

NOTE: This recipe is an excellent way to use turkey leftovers.

Per Serving: 358 Calories; 18g Fat; 36g Protein; 13g Carbohydrate

Cabbage Casserole

4	eggs	beaten
1	pound	smoked ham
1	packet	Ideal Protein Chicken Soup prepared
8	cups	cabbage sliced
1/2	teaspoon	marjoram
2	teaspoons	olive oil
1	teaspoon	garlic powder
1	teaspoon	onion powder
1/2	teaspoon	pepper

In olive oil, sauté the smoked ham. Add cabbage. Cook slowly with onion powder, garlic, marjoram and pepper. When tender, add soup. Allow to cool then add eggs. Pour mixture into an oiled gratin dish and bake in 350 degree oven until eggs are set.

Per Serving: 356 Calories; 16g Fat; 37g Protein; 14g Carbohydrate

Grilled Vegetable Platter
with Turkey

Stuffed Mushrooms

1 1/2	pounds ham julienned
1/2	packet Ideal Protein Salt and Vinegar Ridges crushed
4	large Portobello caps
3	cups portobello mushrooms chopped
1	cup cucumber chopped
1	cup radish
2	cups greens
1	tablespoon green onions chopped
	cloves garlic minced
2	tablespoons Walden Farms Balsamic Vinaigrette Dressing
1	teaspoon olive oil
	sea salt to taste
	pepper to taste

Marinate the 4 large mushroom caps with olive oil and garlic.

Chop the remaining mushrooms. Slowly cook green onions in olive oil marinade (from the mushrooms). Add chopped mushrooms to pan and cook until all water is evaporated. Add chopped garlic and cook for 1 minute. Add dressing and ham, mix well.

Place mushroom heads on a greased cookie sheet and stuff with mixture. Top with crushed Ridges. Bake in a 375-degree oven for 5 to 10 minutes or until lightly browned. Serve on salad with cucumber and radish.

Per Serving: 417 Calories; 21g Fat; 38g Protein; 22g Carbohydrate

Creamy Parsley Dip
Protein Platter

1/2	pound	smoked turkey breast	1	cup	radish
1/3	pound	beef tenderloin, roasted	6	tablespoons	parsley chopped
1/2	pound	shrimp cooked, peeled, deveined	1	clove	garlic minced
1/2	pound	scallops cooked	1/2	cup	Walden Farms Mayonnaise
3	cups	broccoli florets (raw)	1	tablespoon	Walden Farms Honey Dijon Dressing
2	cups	celery 3" sticks	1/2	teaspoon	sea salt
2	cups	cucumber 3" sticks	1/4	teaspoon	pepper

DIP:
Mix parsley, mayonnaise and garlic. Add dressing and seasoning. Cover and refrigerate for at least 2 hours.

Prepare raw small florets of broccoli.
Arrange raw vegetables, sliced cooked meat and seafood on a platter with dip.

Per Serving: 366 Calories; 14g Fat; 47g Protein; 10g Carbohydrate

....

Radish and Vegetable Hot and
Sour Bowl with Shrimp

2	pounds	shrimp fresh, peeled and deveined	1/4	teaspoon	ginger minced
6	cups	chicken broth	2	teaspoons	Walden Farms Orange Spread chopped
2	cups	spinach leaves shredded	1/4	cup	cider vinegar
4	cups	radish sliced	1/4	teaspoon	ground red pepper
2	cups	green onions sliced			

In a large saucepan over medium heat, bring broth to a boil. Stir in vinegar, red pepper and ginger. Add shrimp. Cook until shrimp turn pink and curl, 3 to 4 minutes.

Turn off heat. Stir in radishes, spinach and green onions.
Cover and let stand 2 to 3 minutes before serving.

Per Serving: 352 Calories; 6g Fat; 55g Protein; 13g Carbohydrate

Mediterranean Mahi Mahi Cold Plate

1 1/2	pounds	mahi mahi steaks
2	cups	arugula
2	cups	cucumber sliced 1/4" thick
2	cups	green peppers sliced 1/4" thick
2	cups	fennel bulb shaved
2	tablespoons	lemon juice
8		oregano leaves
1/4	cup	Walden Farms Italian Dressing
2	tablespoons	olive oil
		sea salt to taste
		pepper to taste

Season fish with sea salt and pepper and sear on both sides in olive oil. (keep sauté oil for seasoning later). Transfer to baking dish and bake covered in a 350-degree oven until completely cooked (about 10 minutes).

Blanch fennel in salted, boiling water with lemon juice for 1 minute. Drain. Refrigerate for 30 minutes.

Before serving, mix cucumber with green peppers and fennel. Combine with dressing. Plate the arugula and arrange vegetable mix on the side.

Top vegetables with cold mahi mahi and drizzle with the olive oil from the fish. Decorate with oregano leaves.

Per Serving: 350 Calories; 15g Fat; 42g Protein; 10g Carbohydrate

Poultry

Tips and tricks

All recipes provide for 4 servings.

When cooking with leeks, remember to always use only the white part of the vegetable.

Never use whole fruits (fresh, frozen or canned) during the weight loss phases of the protocol. Only use fruit flavored products with zero carbohydrates such as Walden Farms.

When using Ideal Protein foods in any recipe, it is important to understand that they do not count towards your total mandatory envelopes per day.

It is very easy to overcook poultry when cooking it in a stir fry.
Please pay extra attention to cooking times.

Lemons or limes are excellent additions to any poultry recipe.
They provide a light touch of acidity and help to enhance the flavor of any dish.

Hey, any questions?
 Find us on Chef Verati facebook page
or write chefverati@idealprotein.com

Bon appétit!

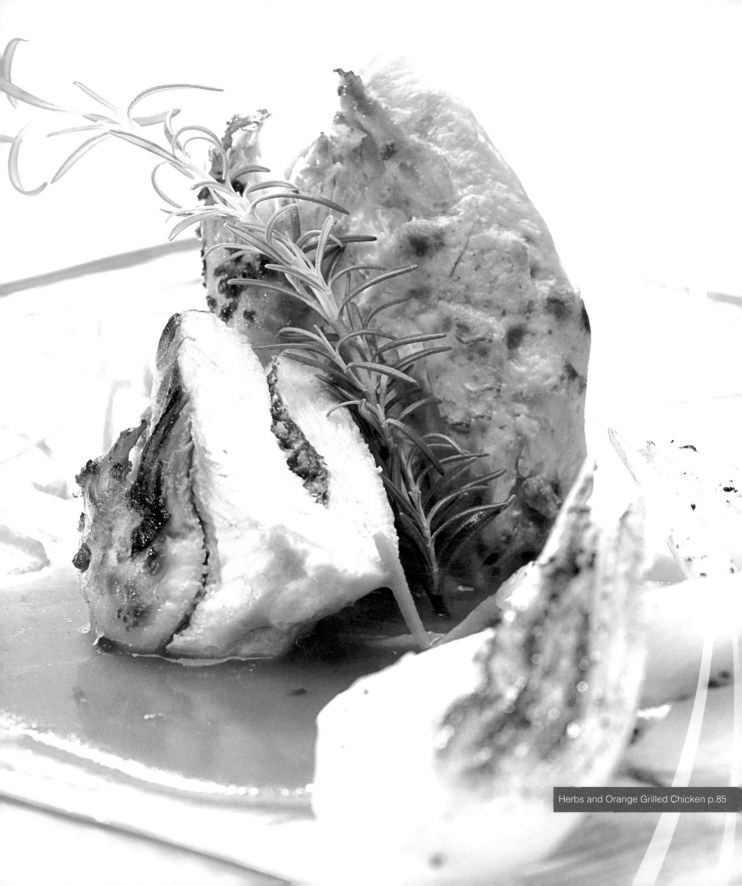

Herbs and Orange Grilled Chicken p.85

Chicken in a Creamy Mustard and Herb Sauce

1 1/2	pounds chicken breast 4 pieces		1/2	cup Dijon mustard
7	cups mushrooms		2	tablespoons olive oil
1	cup green onions sliced thin		2	cloves garlic
1/3	cup chicken stock		1	tablespoon herbs
2/3	cup Walden Farms Honey Dijon Dressing			finely chopped

Heat 1 tablespoon of olive oil in nonstick pan. Cook chicken for 10 minutes until browned on both sides. In same pan, add 1/2 cup green onions and cook for 1 minute. Add stock and bring to a boil. Slow cook for 4 minutes. Reduce liquid to 1 tablespoon.
Mix dressing and mustard in a bowl. Slowly add the warm sauce from the pan on the bowl. Mix well. Return sauce to pan and let simmer (do not boil!) for an additional 5 minutes. Add herbs.

Just before serving, warm 1/2 tablespoon of olive oil in a skillet. Add mushrooms, sauté until soft. Add remaining green onions and garlic. Cook for 2 minutes.
Arrange mushrooms on the plate. Add a slice of chicken breast and top with sauce.

Per Serving: 359 Calories; 21g Fat; 33g Protein; 10g Carbohydrate

Marinated Chicken Breast

1 3/4	pounds chicken breast halved, skinless		4	teaspoons garlic crushed
4	cups cucumber sliced		4	tablespoons grapeseed oil
2	cups radish sliced		6	teaspoons fish sauce
2	cups endive sliced		1/2	teaspoon pepper
2	lemons juiced and zested			

Combine 1/2 of the lemon juice, garlic, 1/2 of the fish sauce and pepper. Coat both sides of chicken breasts. Refrigerate for 30 minutes.
Heat oil on medium heat and add chicken. Sautee for 4 to 5 minutes on each side until cooked. Pour marinade mixture over chicken.
Mix cucumber, radish and endives. Season with olive oil, lemon juice, zest and the other 1/2 of fish sauce.
Serve cold salad with slices of warm chicken.

Per Serving: 353 Calories; 17g Fat; 39g Protein; 12g Carbohydrate

Poultry

Chicken in a Creamy Mustard
and Herb Sauce

Braised Chicken with Mushroom Sauce

1 1/2	pounds	chicken breast diced
1	packet	Ideal Protein Mushroom Soup prepared
4	cups	mushrooms
4	cups	celery root cubed
1		garlic bulb
2	tablespoons	tarragon
4	tablespoons	Walden Farms Alfredo Sauce
2	teaspoons	olive oil
1	tablespoon	onion powder
		turmeric to taste
		sea salt to taste
		pepper to taste

Season chicken with turmeric, salt, pepper and 1 teaspoon of olive oil. Refrigerate for 3 hours. Cut the top of the garlic head and bake with 1 tablespoon of olive oil in a 375-degree oven for 30 minutes, or until soft. Roasted garlic will be used for celery root puree later. Bake chicken in a 350-degree oven, covered for 1 hour.
Remove fat from the baking dish. Transfer meat to a pot and cook on stovetop over low heat until water has evaporated. Add mushrooms, sauté until brown. Add onion powder and cook for an additional minute. Add Alfredo sauce.

Add Mushroom Soup. Simmer and stir until smooth. Transfer all ingredients back to baking dish, cover and bake for an additional 1 1/2 hours on LOW.

Cook celery root in boiling, salted water until tender. Purée with the roasted garlic and the remaining olive oil.

Serve the chicken on a bed of celery root purée.

NOTE: You can make this recipe using various types of mushrooms depending on the season and availability.

Per Serving: 360 Calories; 16g Fat; 36g Protein; 11g Carbohydrate

Cajun Style Chicken Nuggets

1 1/2	pounds	chicken breast cut into 1" pieces
2	cups	alfalfa sprouts
2	cups	green peppers sliced
2	cups	green onions sliced
2	cups	red onion
1	teaspoon	thyme
1	packet	Ideal Protein BBQ Ridges
2	teaspoons	olive oil
1 1/2	teaspoons	chili powder
1	teaspoon	cumin
2	teaspoons	red pepper flakes
1	teaspoon	olive oil
		sea salt to taste
		pepper to taste

Combine thyme, Ridges, Chili powder, cumin and red pepper flakes in large bowl. Dip chicken pieces, coating well. Sauté in 1 teaspoon of oil, turning once until done. Drain excess oil on paper towel.

Cook peppers and green onion in 1 teaspoon olive oil until tender.
Purée the raw red onions. Combine purée with the peppers and green onion. Season.
Serve nuggets on a bed of vegetable puree, top with alfalfa sprouts.

Per Serving: 357 Calories; 17g Fat; 32g Protein; 17g Carbohydrate

Pesto Chicken

1 3/4	pounds chicken breast 4 pieces
8	basil leaves chopped fine
8	cups ok choy cut in 1/2" pieces
2	teaspoons olive oil

PESTO SAUCE

2	tablespoons garlic crushed
6	tablespoons basil leaves chopped fine
4	tablespoons parsley chopped fine
1	tablespoon Walden Farms Blue Cheese Dip
1	tablespoon olive oil
	sea salt to taste
	pepper to taste

Blend all pesto sauce ingredients in a mixer until smooth. Set aside.
Boil bok choy in salted water. Cool in cold water, drain and set aside.
Heat olive oil over medium heat. Fry basil leaves and set aside. Keep one teaspoon of this olive oil. Add chicken and cook over medium heat for 20 minutes. Remove from pan and drain fat.

Add water to the pan and bring to a boil until reduced by half. Add pesto and dip. Simmer for 2 to 3 minutes.

Reheat the chicken and the bok choy in the pesto sauce and serve.

Per Serving: 350 Calories; 21g Fat; 36g Protein; 5g Carbohydrate

Poultry

Sautéed Chicken Liver with Cauliflower Purée

1 3/4	pounds chicken livers cut into 1" pieces		2	tablespoons Walden Farms Alfredo Sauce
7	cups cauliflower cut into small pieces			
1	cup mushrooms sliced		2	tablespoons olive oil
2	teaspoons lemon juice		2	teaspoons onion powder
2	teaspoons minced garlic			sea salt to taste
1	teaspoon rosemary			pepper to taste

Cook cauliflower in salted, boiling water until (just) soft. Drain well and purée. Add Alfredo sauce. Set aside.

In a pan, heat oil on medium-high temperature. Add liver, mushrooms, onion and garlic and cook until mushrooms change color.

Add rosemary and lemon juice. Salt and pepper to taste and cook for an additional 1 to 2 minutes.

Per Serving: 363 Calories; 15g Fat; 40g Protein; 18g Carbohydrate

Quick Chicken Teriyaki

2	pounds chicken breast halved skinless		2	teaspoons fresh ginger minced
5 1/2	cups soybean sprouts		2	cloves garlic pressed
2	cups green peppers		1/4	cup soy sauce, low sodium
4	tablespoons green onions sliced on an angle		1	tablespoon sesame oil

Place chicken pieces in a nonstick 9" square baking dish.
Mix garlic, half of the ginger and soy sauce. Pour over chicken. Cover and refrigerate for 1 hour.
Preheat oven to 350 degrees.
Remove chicken from the marinade.
Bake chicken uncovered for 15 minutes. Turn and bake for an additional 10 to 15 minutes until cooked.
Boil the marinade for 1 minute and set aside.
Sauté green pepper in sesame oil. Add the other half of ginger. Add sprouts and sauté for 4 minutes. The sprouts should be very hot and start to become tender. Do not overcook.
Add the boiling marinade and reduce for 2 minutes.
Slice the chicken breasts and serve on a bed of sprouts. Sprinkle with green onions.

Per Serving: 382 Calories; 12g Fat; 56g Protein; 17g Carbohydrate

Sautéed Chicken Liver with
Cauliflower Purée

Buffalo Chicken Strips

1 1/2	pounds chicken breast cut into strips	1	tablespoon cider vinegar
6	cups celery root cut 1" thick	1	tablespoon Dijon mustard
2	cups cauliflower	1	teaspoon celery seed
1/2	cup Walden Farms BBQ Sauce	1	teaspoon red pepper flakes
1	teaspoon Worcestershire sauce	1/2	teaspoon cayenne pepper
1	teaspoon Tabasco sauce		sea salt to taste
1 1/2	tablespoons olive oil		pepper to taste

Preheat oven to 375 degrees.
Simmer all ingredients, except chicken and vegetables on stovetop over low heat, stirring occasionally. Remove sauce from heat.
Coat chicken with sauce and place on oiled baking sheet. Bake 15 to 20 minutes, or until cooked. Baste with remaining sauce.

Put celery root in cold water with salt. Bring to a boil. Simmer for 20 minutes. Add cauliflower. Cook until both vegetables are tender. Drain.
Purée celery root and cauliflower, season with mustard and olive oil. If needed, add juice from the chicken for a smoother consistency.
Serve chicken on a bed of vegetable purée.

Per Serving: 351 Calories; 20g Fat; 32g Protein; 13g Carbohydrate

....

Sautéed Chicken with Sweet and Sour Blueberry Sauce

1 1/2	pounds chicken breast	2	tablespoons olive oil
1/2	cup chicken broth	1/4	cup cider vinegar
8	cups asparagus blanched	2	teaspoons curry powder
2	tablespoons chopped parsley	1	teaspoon sea salt
1	teaspoon freshly grated ginger	1/2	teaspoon pepper
1	tablespoon Walden Farms Blueberry Spread chopped		

Open chicken breasts and flatten. Season with salt and pepper. Sauté in olive oil for a few minutes then drain excess fat and set aside.
In same pan, combine ginger, blueberry spread and vinegar. Reduce by half. Add chicken stock. Simmer. Return chicken breast to pan to complete cooking.
Blanch asparagus in salted, boiling water. Sauté in olive oil with curry.

Per Serving: 367 Calories; 20g Fat; 35g Protein; 14g Carbohydrate

Buffalo Chicken Strips

Chicken Kabob Skewers

1 1/2	pounds	chicken breast	cubed
2	cups	green peppers	chopped
2	cups	zucchini	sliced 1/2" thick
2	cups	arugula	
2	cups	green onions	sliced 1/8" thick
2	tablespoons	Walden Farms Caesar Salad Dressing	
2	tablespoons	Walden Farms BBQ Sauce	
2	tablespoons	olive oil	
4		wooden skewers	prepared

Preheat grill to medium-high heat.
Thread chicken onto skewers alternating with peppers and zucchini. Brush with olive oil.
Grill 3 to 4 minutes on each side turning frequently until chicken is cooked and vegetables are crispy and tender.
Mix dressing and barbecue sauce until well blended. Add arugula and green onions.
Mix well.
Serve skewers on a bed of salad.

Per Serving: 352 Calories; 20g Fat; 31g Protein; 10g Carbohydrate

Poultry

Smoky Chicken with Leek

2	pounds	chicken breasts skinless
8	cups	leek sliced 1/2" thick
4	tablespoons	Walden Farms Apple Spread chopped
4	tablespoons	Walden Farms Hickory Smoked BBQ Sauce
1	tablespoon	olive oil
1/4	teaspoon	nutmeg
1/4	teaspoon	dry mustard
1/2	teaspoon	sea salt
1/4	teaspoon	pepper
1/4	teaspoon	mace

Blanch leek in salted, boiling water.

Rub each chicken breast with 1 tablespoon of BBQ sauce.

In small bowl, mix seasoning, salt, mace, nutmeg, dry mustard and pepper. Sprinkle on both sides of the chicken and set aside for 5 minutes.

In a nonstick frying pan over medium temperature, heat olive oil for approximately 2 minutes. Add seasoned chicken fillets and cook for 5 minutes. Turn chicken and add blanched leeks. Arrange the leeks so that they touch the bottom and sides of the pan and place the chicken on top. Cook for an additional 5 minutes. Add apple spread. Cook for an additional 4 more minutes or until chicken and leeks are tender.

NOTE: Mace is a spice made from the waxy red covering which covers nutmeg seeds. The flavor is similar to that of nutmeg, with a hint of pepper.

Per Serving: 352 Calories; 6g Fat; 45g Protein; 25g Carbohydrate

Poultry

Spice Marinated Chicken

3	pounds chicken breast boneless
1/2	lime juiced
1	cup Walden Farms Alfredo Sauce
1	tablespoon olive oil
1/2	teaspoon cumin
1 1/2	teaspoons ground turmeric
1/2	teaspoon ground coriander
1/4	teaspoon ground cardamom
1/4	teaspoon pepper
1/2	teaspoon sea salt

SALAD

3	cups spinach leaves washed and dried
2	cups mushrooms sliced
2	green peppers finely julienned
1/2	cup green onions chopped
1	tablespoon lemon juice
1/2	teaspoon thyme chopped
1	clove garlic chopped
2	tablespoons olive oil
1/4	teaspoon sea salt
1/8	teaspoon pepper

Combine Alfredo sauce, turmeric, cumin, coriander, pepper and lime juice in a bowl. Stir well.

Place chicken in large zip-closure freezer bag and add sauce mixture. Refrigerate overnight.

Bring skillet to moderate heat. Remove chicken from marinade and sprinkle lightly with salt. Brush with oil and place on the skillet skin side down. Cook for approximately 10 minutes. Turn and cook for an additional 8 minutes or until golden and crispy. Slice each breast into 4 serving pieces and arrange on top of salad.

SALAD: Sauté mushrooms in olive oil over medium heat until tender. Sprinkle with salt and pepper. Add green onions, garlic and thyme. Drain and set aside.

In large bowl, toss together spinach, mushrooms and green peppers. Season with a mixture of olive oil, lemon juice and seasoning.

Per Serving: 433 Calories; 14g Fat; 65g Protein; 10g Carbohydrate

Chicken Kiev on Braised Red Cabbage

1 1/2	pounds	chicken breast 4 pieces
2		egg whites lightly whisked
1		package Ideal Protein Salt and Vinegar Ridges crushed
7	cups	red cabbage sliced
1/2	cup	green onion chopped
1/2	cup	parsley chopped
2		tablespoons Walden Farms Tomato and Basil Sauce
1		tablespoon olive oil
1		tablespoon cider vinegar
1/8		teaspoon garlic powder
1/2		teaspoon paprika
1		teaspoon caraway seed
		sea salt to taste
		pepper to taste
		wooden skewers prepared

Preheat oven to 425 degrees.
Open chicken breasts by making an incision in the middle. Baste with olive oil.
Sprinkle with garlic powder and paprika. Refrigerate for 1 hour.

Warm olive oil in a pan and add the red cabbage, salt, pepper and caraway. Add vinegar.
Bring to a boil. Add 1 cup of water. Cover and slowly cook until cabbage is tender
(approximately 1 hour).

Combine sauce with green onions. Spoon sauce and green onions in the center of each
chicken breast. Fold chicken breasts over. Fold in sides and secure with wooden skewer.
Mix Ridges, parsley, and paprika. Dip chicken in egg white, then coat with ridges mixture.
Place breasts, seam-side down, in sprayed 9" square baking pan. Bake 35 minutes or
until cooked.

Per Serving: 363 Calories; 18g Fat; 37g Protein; 15g Carbohydrate

Spicy Chicken Sauté

1 3/4	pounds chicken breasts, skinless, boneless
7	cups leek
2	tablespoons fresh lemon juice
1	cup green onions
1	cup Walden Farms Ketchup
1	tablespoon olive oil
1	teaspoon hot pepper sauce

Combine ketchup, 1 cup of water, green onions, lemon juice and hot pepper sauce in small saucepan. Bring to a boil. Reduce heat, simmer uncovered for 5 to 10 minutes, stirring occasionally. Keep warm.
Prepare the grill. Place chicken on grid, turning occasionally. Brush sauce over chicken during grilling and cover.

Cut leek into 2" long tubes. Blanch in salted, boiling water for 2 minutes. Baste with olive oil, seasoning and grill.

> **NOTE: There is a popular saying: "Food is better cooked on an open flame". This is not true, food should never be in direct contact with flames.**

Per Serving: 369 Calories; 9g Fat; 47g Protein; 24g Carbohydrate

---

Crispy Chicken

1 3/4	pounds chicken breast
1	egg white lightly whisked
1	packet Ideal Protein Salt and Vinegar Ridges coarsely crushed
4	cups celery root cubed
4	cups leek chopped
1	tablespoon Walden Farms Honey Dijon Dressing
1	teaspoon olive oil
1	teaspoon Dijon mustard
	sea salt to taste
	pepper to taste

Preheat oven to 400 degrees.
Baste chicken with mustard. Dip each piece into egg whites and coat with Ridges. Place on oiled cookie sheet. Baste with olive oil. Bake 40 minutes or until chicken is cooked.
In a pan, sweat leek in olive oil until tender. Add celery root. Cover with water and cook until tender. Drain and purée until smooth. Add seasoning and mustard dressing.

Per Serving: 402 Calories; 17g Fat; 40g Protein; 21g Carbohydrate

Herbs and Orange Grilled Chicken

1 1/2	pounds chicken breast
8	fennel bulbs
3	cloves garlic minced
2	teaspoons orange peel grated
1	teaspoon thyme chopped fine
1	teaspoon rosemary chopped fine
1/2	cup Walden Farms Orange Spread chopped
1	tablespoon Worcestershire sauce
2	tablespoons olive oil
3	tablespoons cider vinegar
1	teaspoon sea salt
1/2	teaspoon pepper

In a small bowl, mix garlic, grated orange peel, salt, thyme, rosemary and pepper. Make an incision in each chicken breast. Spoon 1/4 of herb mixture in each breast.

Combine orange spread, Worcestershire sauce and vinegar.
Place chicken on hot and oiled grill, approximately 8" from heat. Cook, turning and basting with orange mixture every 5 minutes, for approximately 30 minutes or until chicken is cooked.

Quarter fennel bulbs. Blanch in salted, boiling water. Grill while basting

Per Serving: 359 Calories; 20g Fat; 31g Protein; 16g Carbohydrate

Tangy Chicken with Portobello Crust

1 3/4	pounds chicken breasts skinless boneless
2	cups button mushrooms trimmed and sliced
3	cups portobello mushrooms trimmed and sliced
1	cup green onions peeled and chopped
1	clove garlic minced
1	tablespoon fresh chervil minced
3	tablespoons olive oil
1	teaspoon sea salt
1/2	teaspoon pepper

TANGY SAUCE

2	cups chicken stock
2	cups green onions chopped
4	tablespoons Walden Farms Orange Spread chopped
1	cup Walden Farms Balsamic Vinaigrette Dressing
2	tablespoons Walden Farms Tomato and Basil Sauce
1	teaspoon olive oil

In a large heavy frying pan, warm olive oil over medium high heat. Add button and portobello mushrooms, green onions and garlic. Cook until light golden color, approximately 5 minutes, stirring occasionally. Cool. Season.

Remove small fillets from underside of chicken breasts and place in food processor. Grind to smooth paste, pulsing on/off. Add mushroom mixture and chop on "coarse". Place chicken breasts between two sheets of wax paper and gently pound to even thickness.

Divide mushroom mixture into 4 parts (approximately 1/2 cup each).
On 12" length plastic wrap, place one part of mushroom mixture in center. Fold plastic over mixture. Use a rolling pin to roll out the mixture, ensuring the size is slightly larger than each chicken breast. Place chicken, smooth rounded side down, on top of mushroom mixture. Gather plastic around chicken (as if wrapping a gift basket) until mixture adheres to top and sides of chicken. Creating a crust. Gently unwrap and invert chicken, uncoated side down, onto a baking sheet lined with parchment paper.
(This can be prepared ahead and refrigerated).

TANGY SAUCE: Cook green onions in olive oil add spread and stock. Simmer for 5 minutes. Add Tomato and Basil sauce and cook for an additional 5 minutes. Add dressing. Serve on the side with chicken.

Per Serving: 363 Calories; 14g Fat; 43g Protein; 16g Carbohydrate

Chicken Breast with Blue Cheese and Pepper Sauce

1 1/2	pounds	chicken breast skinless, boneless
4	cups	cabbage leaves blanched
4	leafs	fresh basil
1	clove	garlic
1	teaspoon	rosemary
4	leafs	fresh sage
1/4	cup	Walden Farms Blue Cheese Dip
		sea salt to taste
		pepper to taste

SAUCE

3 1/2		green peppers sliced
1/2	tablespoon	green onions sliced
2	tablespoons	olive oil
		sea salt to taste
		pepper to taste

Sprinkle chicken breasts with salt and pepper. Baste with dip. Place 1 basil leaf and 1 sage leaf on each piece of chicken. Wrap chicken with 2 or 3 cabbage leaves.
In large saucepan with steamer rack, place approx. 1" of water. Add garlic and rosemary to the water and bring to a boil. Arrange chicken on steamer rack. Cover and cook on high heat for approximately 20 minutes, or until chicken is completely cooked. Make sure the water doesn't completely evaporate. Place chicken on serving plate and pour sauce around it.

Sauce: slice 1/2 of the green peppers and all the green onions. Extract juice. In small saucepan, place the other 1/2 of peppers and juice, olive oil, salt and pepper. Bring to a boil.

NOTE: If you do not have a juicer, you can use a blender and pass the liquid through a sieve.

Per Serving: 357 Calories; 20g Fat; 31g Protein; 12g Carbohydrate

Chicken Stuffed Peppers

1 1/2	pounds chicken breast cooked and shredded		1	tablespoon fresh ginger minced
2	egg whites whisked		2	cloves garlic minced
4	whole green peppers		1	tablespoon sesame oil
4	cups red peppers chopped		1 1/2	tablespoons soy sauce
2	cups green onions thinly sliced			

Cut the top off of each whole pepper, remove seeds. Place peppers in boiling water and boil for 5 minutes. Drain and set aside.

Heat pan and add sesame oil. Add garlic and ginger root. Mix for 30 seconds. Add chopped peppers and green onions and stir fry for an additional 2 minutes. Remove from heat. Add chicken and remaining ingredients. Combine well.

Spoon 3/4 cup of this mixture into each reserved pepper. Surround the peppers with the rest of the stuffing. Cover and bake in a 350-degrees oven for 30 minutes or until thoroughly heated.

> **NOTE: This dish is easy to prepare in advance and may be frozen.**

Per Serving: 367 Calories; 17g Fat; 34g Protein; 22g Carbohydrate

Grilled Chicken with Colorful Salad

1 3/4	pounds chicken breast		1	teaspoon fresh ginger grated
12	lettuce leaves		2	cups radish thinly sliced
1	cup soybean sprouts blanched			parsley
1	cup green peppers cut in 1/4" strips		1	cup Walden Farms
1	cup green onions chopped			Sesame Ginger Dressing
2	cups red onions sliced fine			

Place chicken on prepared grill for approximately 5 minutes per side until cooked. Chill in refrigerator. Cut into 1/4" strips.
In large mixing bowl, place cooled chicken, peppers, green onions and blanched sprouts. Add dressing and toss gently to mix well.
Serve on lettuce leaves.

Per Serving: 358 Calories; 16g Fat; 38g Protein; 15g Carbohydrate

Chicken Stuffed Peppers

Leek and Spinach Chicken Breast

1 1/2	pounds chicken breast
4	cups chicken stock
4	cups leek white part only
4	cups spinach
2	teaspoons garlic crushed
5	teaspoons Walden Farms Orange Spread chopped
2	tablespoons Walden Farms Honey Dijon Dressing
1 1/2	tablespoons olive oil
	sea salt to taste
	pepper to taste

Clean the white part of the leeks. Cut into 2" pieces. In a pot, coat the leeks with ½ of the orange spread and chicken stock. Cover and bring to simmer. Reduce and simmer for approximately 30 minutes (or until a knife can go through the leek without resistance). Remove leeks.

Reduce the liquid until it coats the back of the spoon. Reheat the leeks in this sauce. Slice on an angle to serve.

Cut chicken breast into 4 portions and sauté in pan with olive oil.
Mix remaining orange spread and honey Dijon dressing with garlic. Baste chicken with mixture and cook for 7 to 8 minutes. Salt and pepper to taste.
Sauté spinach just before serving.

Place tubes of leek on the plate and arrange spinach in the middle. Top with chicken.

Per Serving: 364 Calories; 18g Fat; 32g Protein; 15g Carbohydrate

Chicken and Cauliflower Salad

1 1/2	pounds	chicken breast
6	cups	cauliflower chopped
4	cups	mixed greens
1	cup	green peppers cut 1/4" thick
1	cup	green onions sliced
1		jalapeno peppers chopped
1/2	cup	lemon juice
1	clove	garlic crushed
1 1/2	tablespoons	olive oil
2	tablespoons	parsley chopped
2	teaspoons	chili powder
		sea salt to taste
		pepper to taste

Brush chicken with olive oil and season with salt, pepper and chili powder.
Cook in a 375-degree oven for approximately 30 mins or until cooked. Remove and let cool. Cut chicken into cubes.
Blanch cauliflower in salted, boiling water.
Combine chicken with cooked cauliflower. Add peppers, jalapeño, green onions and garlic. Refrigerate until ready to serve.

Just before serving, add lemon juice, chili powder, parsley and olive oil, serve with greens.

Per Serving: 350 Calories; 18g Fat; 33g Protein; 16g Carbohydrate

Chicken Cretons

2	pounds chicken breast ground	1	teaspoon salt
1	cup chicken stock	1	pinch thyme
1/2	envelope Ideal Protein Salt and Vinegar Ridges crushed	1	pinch nutmeg
		6	cups greens
1	teaspoon parsley	4	tablespoons Walden Farms dressing (your choice)
1/2	cup green onion chopped		
1	clove garlic minced	1	cup pickles
2	teaspoons mustard powder		

Combine all ingredients in a large pot except for pickles and greens. Bring to boil, stirring constantly.
Reduce to low heat and cook for 50 minutes or until the stock is completely evaporated.
Divide mixture into individual serving dishes or in a large dish. Refrigerate.
Serve on the greens, with dressing and pickles.

Per Serving: 379 Calories; 18g Fat; 43g Protein; 10g Carbohydrate

Chicken and Shrimps in a Curry Tomato Sauce

1 1/4	pounds chicken breast 4 pieces	2	cups Walden Farms Tomato and Basil Sauce
1/2	pound shrimp cooked		
4	cups green peppers cubed	1	tablespoon olive oil
4	cups broccoli	3	teaspoons curry powder
2	cloves garlic crushed	1 1/2	teaspoons sea salt
2	teaspoons parsley chopped	1 1/2	teaspoon pepper
2	teaspoons fresh thyme leaves chopped fine		

In large plastic bag, combine curry, 1 teaspoon of the salt and pepper. Add chicken, one piece at a time, shaking to coat. In a large frying pan, heat oil on medium temperature. Add chicken and turn after 5 minutes. Cook until brown on all sides. Remove chicken from pan and keep warm.
In the same frying pan, add green peppers and garlic. Stir-fry for approximately 5 minutes. Add remaining 1/2 teaspoon of salt, pepper, curry powder, Tomato and Basil sauce, parsley and thyme.
Transfer chicken and shrimp to a large baking dish and cover with tomato sauce mixture. Place in a 375-degree oven and cook for approximately 30 minutes or until chicken is cooked through. Remove chicken and place on large serving platter.

Per Serving: 354 Calories; 16g Fat; 39g Protein; 15g Carbohydrate

Chicken Cretons

Chicken Teriyaki with Cucumber Salad

1 1/2	pounds	chicken breast
8	cups	cucumber sliced 1/8" thick
4	tablespoons	Walden Farms Creamy Italian Dressing
1/3	cup	Walden Farms Honey BBQ Sauce
2	tablespoons	olive oil
5	tablespoons	teriyaki sauce
1	teaspoon	garlic salt
		sea salt to taste
		pepper to taste

Marinate chicken in teriyaki sauce, garlic and BBQ sauce for at least 1 hour.
Sprinkle cucumber with salt. Set aside for 1 hour. Rinse salt and dry. Mix with dressing.
Sauté chicken breast in olive oil until cooked. Slice. Fan slices on cucumber salad

Per Serving: 352 Calories; 20g Fat; 31g Protein; 10g Carbohydrate

....

Cream of Mushroom Soup

1 1/2	pounds	chicken breast cooked, sliced
3 1/2	cups	chicken stock
1	package	Ideal Protein Mushroom Soup prepared
6	cups	mushrooms chopped
2	cups	celery root chopped
2	teaspoons	parsley chopped
1	tablespoon	lemongrass
1	tablespoon	olive oil
1	teaspoon	onion powder
		sea salt to taste
		pepper to taste

Sauté mushrooms in olive oil. Add celery root and onion powder. Add chicken stock,
Mushroom soup and simmer for 20 minutes. Season.
Remove mushrooms, blend and return to soup. If necessary add water to achieve desired
consistency.

Before serving, add chicken and season.

Per Serving: 354 Calories; 17g Fat; 36g Protein; 9g Carbohydrate

Chicken Teriyaki with
Cucumber Salad

Chili Chicken Stir-fry

1 1/2	pounds chicken breast cooked cubed		1	tablespoon cider vinegar	
2	cups green onions sliced		1	tablespoon hot sauce	
2	cups Chinese cabbage finely sliced		2	tablespoons tamari soy sauce	
2	cups portobello mushrooms quartered		1/4	teaspoon chili paste	
2	cups soybean sprouts		1/2	tablespoon chili powder	
1	tablespoon vegetable oil		2	tablespoons fresh Ginger	

Combine cubed chicken with ginger and chili. Refrigerate for 30 minutes. Heat oil in wok and stir-fry chicken 3 to 4 minutes, until warm.
Add mushrooms, soybean sprouts and cabbage. Add vinegar, chili paste and sauces.
Add scallions. Heat thoroughly and serve immediately.

Per Serving: 365 Calories; 19g Fat; 38g Protein

Toriwasa

2	pounds chicken breast skinless boneless		2	teaspoons cider vinegar	
2	tablespoons chicken stock		2 1/2	teaspoons wasabi	
4	cups soybean sprouts		1	sheet Nori shredded	
3	cups zucchini finely diced		2	tablespoons soy sauce	
1	cup green onions		1/2	teaspoon sea salt	
4	ounces Italian parsley				
2	teaspoons sesame oil				

Cut chicken breasts horizontally into paper thin slices, then into 1/4" wide shreds. Place chicken, chicken stock, cider vinegar, 1/8 teaspoon salt into a small saucepan. Bring to a boil. Remove from heat and let cool to room temperature.
Boil 2 1/2 cups water and 1/2 teaspoon salt in a small pan. Cook parsley for 1 minute. Drain and rinse under cold water.

TO ASSEMBLE: combine the wasabi paste with 2 tablespoons of soy sauce into a mixing bowl. Stir in chicken, liquid and parsley. Mix thoroughly. Divide into 4 small bowls and cover with shredded nori.

Sauté zucchini in 1 teaspoon of sesame oil until golden colored. Add green onions and soybean sprouts. Serve on the side.

Per Serving: 352 Calories; 10g Fat; 54g Protein; 14g Carbohydrate

Chili Chicken Stir-fry

Chinese Chicken Salad

1 1/2	pounds chicken breast cooked and shredded		3	tablespoons soy sauce
2	cups celery stalks chopped		1	teaspoon onion powder
2	cups romaine lettuce sliced		1	teaspoon ginger ground
2	cups soybean sprouts cooked and drained		1/4	teaspoon sea salt
2	cups green onions sliced		1/4	teaspoon pepper
1/4	cup Walden Farms French Dressing		1 1/2	tablespoons olive oil
2	cups Walden Farms Mayonnaise			

Combine all ingredients together except romaine lettuce.
Plate salad greens and top with mixture.
Decorate with green onions

NOTE: This meal is easy and quick to prepare.

Per Serving: 362 Calories; 20g Fat; 36g Protein; 12g Carbohydrate

---

Tart and Fruity Grilled Chicken

2	pounds chicken breast skinless		1/2	cup apple cider
2	large endives		4	tablespoons soy sauce
3	cups green onions chopped		3/4	teaspoon sea salt
1/4	cup Walden Farms Orange Spread chopped		1/2	teaspoon pepper
3	tablespoons olive oil			

Warm olive oil in a small fry pan over medium temperature. Add green onions, cook, stirring until tender for approximately 5 minutes. Stir in vinegar, soy sauce and orange spread. Pour mixture into food processor or blender and blend approximately 1 minute.

Sprinkle chicken with salt and pepper and arrange in a shallow bowl in a single layer. Pour sauce over chicken, cover and refrigerate for at least 2 hours.

When you are ready to cook, place chicken on a prepared grill approximately 8" from heat. Heat marinade in small saucepan on grill or stovetop to boiling then simmer.
Grill chicken, turning and basting with sauce every 10 minutes, for approximately 30 minutes or until chicken is cooked.
Baste blanched endives while grilling, just like with the chicken.

Per Serving: 450 Calories; 27g Fat; 40g Protein; 11g Carbohydrate

Poultry

Chinese Chicken Salad

Curry Pot

2.2	pounds chicken breast		2	tablespoons Walden Farms Fruit Spread	
1 1/2	cups chicken broth				
2	cups cauliflower small pieces		1/4	cup Walden Farms Chipotle Ranch Dressing	
1	cup cucumber diced				
3	cups celery root sliced 1/2" thick		1 1/2	tablespoons olive oil	
2	cups green onions sliced		1	tablespoon curry paste	
1	tablespoon fresh ginger ground				

Coat chicken with curry paste and place in a shallow dish. Refrigerate for 10 minutes. Heat oil in skillet on medium-high heat. Add chicken. Add celery root, green onions and fresh ginger. Cook for 10 to 15 minutes (or until chicken is cooked). Stir in vegetables after 5 minutes. Add broth. Add blanched cauliflower and bring to a boil. Remove from heat. Add fruit spread and dressing while stirring constantly. Cover and let stand for 10 minutes.
Just before serving, sprinkle with diced cucumber.

Per Serving: 361 Calories; 20g Fat; 33g Protein; 11g Carbohydrate

Chicken with Grape and Apricot Sauce

			1	tablespoon Dijon mustard	
2	pounds chicken breast 4 pieces		1	tablespoon olive oil	
4	large endives large		1	tablespoon cider vinegar	
1	cup Walden Farms Apricot Spread chopped				
1	cup Walden Farms Grape Spread chopped				

Sear chicken breasts in olive oil. Season to taste. Cook in a 375-degree oven for 15 minutes or until cooked. Keep warm.

In a large skillet, combine apricot spread, grape spread, vinegar and mustard. Mix well and bring to a boil. Reduce heat. Simmer for 10 minutes. Baste chicken with this sauce. Return to oven at 400 degrees and bake for an additional 5 minutes.
Blanch endives in salted, boiling water. Drain. Cut in quarters. Sauté in olive oil and add glaze 5 minutes before end of cooking.

Per Serving: 356 Calories; 20g Fat; 38g Protein; trace Carbohydrate

Curry Pot

Breaded Turkey Scallopini in Tomato and Basil Sauce

1 3/4	pounds turkey breast cutlets 4 pieces	8	tablespoons Walden Farms Tomato and Basil Sauce
2	egg whites	1 1/2	tablespoons Dijon mustard
2	packages Ideal Protein Southwest Cheese Curls crushed	3	tablespoons olive oil sea salt to taste pepper to taste
6	cups asparagus		
2	cups celery sliced 1/2" thick		
2	tablespoons garlic crushed		
2	teaspoons thyme		

Pre-heat oven to 375 degrees.
Wisk egg whites. In a separate bowl combine mustard and curls for breading.
Dip each piece of turkey into egg whites and then breading. In a hot pan, sauté until golden brown. Transfer cutlets to a baking dish and arrange side by side.

Blanch celery root in salted, boiling water. Remove, set water aside.
Cook asparagus in celery root water.

Pour Tomato and Basil sauce over meat. Add slices of celery root and asparagus. Add the remaining Tomato and Basil sauce. Sprinkle with thyme. Bake uncovered for 30 minutes.

Per Serving: 365 Calories; 13g Fat; 50g Protein; 14g Carbohydrate

Poultry

Caribbean Broiled Turkey

1 3/4	pounds turkey breast	2	tablespoons Walden Farms
1	tablespoon olive oil		Apricot Spread chopped
7	cups green onion	2	teaspoons hot pepper sauce
3	tablespoons garlic crushed	1	tablespoon soy sauce
2	tablespoons lime juice		sea salt to taste
2	teaspoons lime peel zested		pepper to taste

In a food processor or blender, purée green onions, garlic, hot pepper sauce, olive oil, pepper, salt, lime juice, lime zest and soy sauce. Puree will be used to fill and baste turkey pieces.

Cut turkey into 1/2" slices. Make an incision in turkey pieces and fill with ½ of purée.
To broil: Place turkey pieces on greased broiler pan. Broil 6 minutes. Turn over. Baste with purée and return to broiler for approximately 5 minutes. Baste with purée again and broil for an additional 4 to 5 minutes until meat reaches 170 degrees on meat thermometer.

Per Serving: 378 Calories; 16g Fat; 43g Protein; 16g Carbohydrate

Braised Turkey Breast with Celery Root

2	pounds turkey breast cutlets	12	ounces Walden Farms
6	cups celery root diced 1/2" thick		Tomato and Basil Sauce
2	cups zucchini cut 1/2" thick	3	tablespoons olive oil
2	tablespoons parsley chopped fine	1	tablespoon onion powder
1	teaspoon oregano	1	teaspoon garlic salt
1	teaspoon basil		sea salt to taste
			pepper to taste

In a pan, brown turkey in olive oil. Transfer to a baking dish and sprinkle with onion powder. In same pan, heat Tomato and Basil sauce. Season. Pour over turkey. Cover and bake in a 325-degree oven for 2 hours, basting once or twice. Add celery root. Cover and bake for an additional 30 minutes.

Keep turkey and vegetables warm in a serving dish.
Using the drippings from the baking dish for sauce. Add water if too thick.
Sauté zucchini in Olive oil. Plate turkey and vegetable, cover with sauce and sprinkle with parsley.

Per Serving: 363 Calories; 13g Fat; 51g Protein; 11g Carbohydrate

Caribbean Broiled Turkey

Cozy Lime Turkey

1 1/2	pounds	turkey breast
7	cups	mushrooms sliced
1	cup	enoki mushroom
1/2	cup	lime juice
2 1/2	tablespoons	olive oil
1/2	teaspoon	sea salt
1/2	teaspoon	pepper

In a small bowl, mix lime juice and 1 1/2 tablespoons of olive oil. Dip each turkey piece until coated. On a baking sheet, arrange turkey in single layer; sprinkle with salt and pepper. Arrange oven rack at least 6" from heat and set temperature to broil. Broil turkey approximately 15 minutes, turn and pour remaining lime-oil mixture over chicken. Continue to broil approximately 15 minutes or until turkey is cooked.
Sauté mushrooms in remaining olive oil. Add seasoning.
Serve turkey on a bed of mushrooms.

Per Serving: 361 Calories; 20g Fat; 37g Protein; 10g Carbohydrate

....

Crusted Turkey Breast with Asparagus

1 3/4	pounds	turkey breast 4 pieces
2		egg whites lightly whisked
2	packets	Ideal Protein Salt and Vinegar Ridges crushed
6	cups	asparagus
2	cups	green onions sliced
4	tablespoons	lemon juice
1	teaspoon	olive oil
4	tablespoons	Dijon mustard

Combine Dijon mustard with lemon juice, green onions, Ridges and lightly whisked egg whites.
Make a lengthways incision in each turkey breast. Season inside and outside. Fill each with mixture. Top with any leftover mixture. Bake in a 375-degree oven for 30 minutes (or until cooked) and tops are crispy.
Cook asparagus in salted, boiling water. Remove and baste with olive oil.
Serve turkey on a bed of asparagus.

Per Serving: 455 Calories; 17g Fat; 55g Protein; 22g Carbohydrate

Poultry

Cozy Lime Turkey

Garlic Turkey Chinese Style

1 1/2	pounds turkey breast
3	tablespoons chicken stock
2	cups broccolini cut 1.5" long
2	cups fennel cut 1.5" long
2	cups green onions cut 1.5" long
1	cup mung bean shoots
1/2	cup garlic crushed
2	teaspoons sesame oil
3	tablespoons soy sauce
1/2	teaspoon sea salt

Cut turkey into strips. Sauté in sesame oil for a few minutes. Add garlic, fennel, broccolini, green onions and mung bean shoots. Add stock and soy sauce. Cover and cook until turkey and vegetables are cooked. Remove meat and vegetables. Reduce sauce. Return turkey and vegetables to pan. Combine well and serve.

Per Serving: 354 Calories; 15g Fat; 40g Protein; 17g Carbohydrate

....

Honey-Mustard Turkey Meatballs

2	pounds turkey breast ground	2	tablespoons Walden Farms Honey Dijon Dressing
2	egg whites lightly whisked		
1	package Ideal Protein Salt and Vinegar Ridges crushed	1	cup Walden Farms Orange Spread chopped
6	cups celery root	1	teaspoon Dijon mustard
1	cup green onions	1	tablespoon onion powder
1	teaspoon fresh ginger	1/2	teaspoon ground ginger
1	cup chopped green pepper		

In a bowl, combine turkey, egg whites, Ridges, green onions and dressing. Form into 30 1" balls. Place balls on a greased 13"x9"x2" baking dish. Bake, uncovered at 350 degrees for 20 to 25 minutes or until juice runs clear.
In a saucepan, combine spread, green peppers and onion powder. Bring to a boil, stirring constantly. Cook and stir an additional 2 minutes. Stir in mustard until smooth.
Brush meatballs with approximately 1/4 cup of sauce and return to the oven for 10 minutes.

Serve remaining sauce as a dip for the meatballs.

Per Serving: 423 Calories; 16g Fat; 53g Protein; 16g Carbohydrate

Garlic Turkey Chinese Style

Lime Turkey Skewers

1 1/2	pounds turkey breast cut into strips	4	tablespoons Dijon mustard
4	cups leek sliced fine	1	teaspoon olive oil
4	cups fennel sliced fine	1	teaspoon paprika
4	limes	1	teaspoon pepper
1	tablespoon thyme chopped fine	1	teaspoon sea salt
1/2	cup Walden Farms Jersey Sweet Onion Dressing		wooden skewers

Cut 2 limes in half and rub over the turkey.
Cover turkey generously with dressing and season with thyme, salt and pepper.
Thread skewers with turkey strips.
Cook over medium temperature for 5 to 8 minutes. After 4 to 5 minutes, baste with mustard.

Cook fennel and leek in olive oil until crisp. Add lime juice and paprika.

Per Serving: 359 Calories; 13g Fat; 37g Protein; 25g Carbohydrate

Tomato and Turkey Mushroom Caps

1 1/2	pounds turkey breast ground	1/2	teaspoon oregano chopped fine
1	packet Ideal Protein Salt and Vinegar Ridges crushed	1/2	teaspoon thyme leaves chopped fine
2	cups green onions chopped fine	1/4	cup Walden Farms Tomato and Basil Sauce
2	cups green peppers chopped fine	1	tablespoon olive oil
8	whole mushrooms large caps		sea salt to taste
2	cloves garlic minced		pepper to taste
1	tablespoon parsley chopped fine		

Preheat oven to 350 degrees.
Clean mushrooms. Season.
Heat oil in a skillet. Sauté meat, green onions, garlic, parsley and peppers for 5 minutes.
Season. Add oregano and thyme, mix and cook for 4 minutes. Add Ridges to meat mixture. Cook for 2 minutes while stirring.
Fill mushrooms and place in oven-safe dish. Bake for 15 minutes.

Per Serving: 366 Calories; 16g Fat; 41g Protein; 16g Carbohydrate

Lime Turkey Skewers

Raspberry Glazed Turkey

1 1/2	pounds turkey breast	4	Stash Tea Wild Raspberry Tea bags
8	cups fennel bulbs	2	tablespoons olive oil
2	tablespoons Walden Farms Balsamic Vinaigrette Dressing		
3	tablespoons Walden Farms Raspberry Spread chopped		

Preheat oven to 350 degrees.
Infuse tea bags in 1 cup of water. Mix with dressing and spread. Set 2 tablespoons of mixture aside.

In a baking dish, pour mixture over turkey breast and bake for 45 minutes or until liquid is evaporated and turkey is cooked.
Slowly cook fennel in olive oil, covered for approximately 20 minutes. When tender, add the reserved glaze and simmer for an additional 5 minutes.

Per Serving: 354 Calories; 18g Fat; 36g Protein; 13g Carbohydrate

....

Turkey and Chicken Liver Pâté

1 1/4	pounds turkey breast ground	1	teaspoon celery leaves chopped
3/4	pound chicken liver ground	2	teaspoons olive oil
1	egg white	3/4	teaspoon sea salt
7 1/2	cups red cabbage sliced	1/2	teaspoon pepper
1/2	cup green onions chopped	3/4	teaspoon red pepper
1	teaspoon dried parsley		

Mix meats with parsley, celery and seasoning. Incorporate egg white. Prepare mixture into 8 patties. Sauté in a pan on both sides for a few minutes and finish in the oven for 10 to 15 minutes.
Cook green onions in olive oil. Add red cabbage and seasoning. Add 1 cup of water.
Cook covered until tend.
Top red cabbage with patties.

Per Serving: 381 Calories; 15g Fat; 47g Protein; 14g Carbohydrate

Raspberry Glazed Turkey

Sweet and Sour Turkey

1 1/2	pounds turkey breast	1	tablespoon olive oil
1	teaspoon chicken stock	1/3	cup cider vinegar
6	cups green peppers cubed	1	tablespoon soy sauce
2	cups green onions cubed	1/2	teaspoon garlic powder
2	tablespoons ginger minced		
1	teaspoon cilantro chopped fine		
1	cup Walden Farms Jersey Sweet Onion Dressing		
1	cup Walden Farms Orange Spread chopped		

COCK-POT: Arrange vegetables at the bottom of crock-pot. Place turkey on top of vegetables. Combine all other ingredients in a bowl and pour over turkey. Cover crock-pot and cook on low for 8 to 10 hours.

OVEN METHOD: Arrange vegetables at the bottom of a greased baking dish. Add turkey on top. Combine all other ingredients and pour over turkey. Cover pan tightly with foil. Bake at 300 degrees for 2 hours.

Per Serving: 362 Calories; 15g Fat; 37g Protein; 22g Carbohydrate

Turkey and Mushroom Meatballs

1 1/2	pounds ground turkey	4	cups spinach chopped
1	egg white	1	pinch sage powder
2	packages Ideal Protein Mushroom Soup prepared	1	piece bay leaf
1	packet Ideal Protein Salt and Vinegar Ridges crushed	1	teaspoon olive oil
4	cups mushroom chopped		sea salt to taste
			pepper to taste

Heat oil in a skillet over medium-high heat. Add mushrooms and cook until all liquid has evaporated. Add spinach. Mix and remove from heat. Let cool.
In a bowl, combine meat, egg, ridges, mushrooms, spinach, sage and pepper.
Make 1" diameter meatballs. Sauté in skillet over medium-high heat.
Add mushroom soup to pan and simmer for 25 to 30 minutes.

Per Serving: 377 Calories; 17g Fat; 46g Protein; 9g Carbohydrate

Sweet and Sour Turkey

Szechuan-Style Turkey and Broccoli

1 1/2	pounds	turkey breast cut into 1" cubes
6	cups	broccoli flowerets blanched
2	cups	green pepper
2	tablespoons	garlic minced
2	tablespoons	ginger shredded
1/3	cup	Walden Farms Thick 'n Spicy BBQ Sauce
2	tablespoons	olive oil
2	tablespoons	soy sauce

Combine BBQ sauce and soy sauce in small bowl, set aside. Heat oil in wok or large skillet over medium high heat. Add turkey and stir-fry 3 to 4 minutes or until cooked through. Remove with slotted spoon.

Add oil, green onions, garlic and ginger to skillet. Stir-fry 30 seconds. Add broccoli and peppers. Stir-fry 3 minutes or until vegetables are crispy and tender. Add turkey and sauce mixture. Stir-fry approximately 1 minute or until sauce thickens.

Per Serving: 373 Calories; 18g Fat; 38g Protein; 15g Carbohydrate

Turkey and Vegetable Stir-Fry

1 1/2	pounds	turkey breast strips
1	cup	zucchini finely chopped
1	cup	celery thinly sliced
2	cups	sprouted soybeans
1	cup	mushrooms sliced
2	cups	green onions thinly sliced
2	teaspoons	lemon juice

1	clove	garlic
1/2	teaspoon	fresh ginger grated
1	tablespoon	sesame oil
2	tablespoons	soy sauce
		sea salt to taste
		pepper to taste

Heat garlic in sesame oil for 1 minute. Do not burn. Remove from pan and set aside. Add turkey. Cook until golden. Add celery, green onions and ginger to the pan and cook for an additional 2 minutes. Add zucchini, soybeans and mushrooms. Cook for 1 minute. Combine soy sauce and lemon juice. Add to pan.
Cook and stir until sauce reduces and thickens. Season.

Per Serving: 352 Calories; 17g Fat; 40g Protein; 11g Carbohydrate

Szechuan-Style Turkey and Broccoli

Turkey Casserole Mediterranean Style

1 1/2	pounds turkey breast 4 pieces		2	teaspoons garlic crushed
1/4	tablespoon chicken stock		1	teaspoon oregano
4	cups green peppers cut 1/4" thick		4	tablespoons parsley chopped fine
4	cups zucchini cut 1/4" thick		2	tablespoons olive oil
1/4	cup lemon juice		1	tablespoon onion powder

Sauté turkey in olive oil in a wok or pan. When half cooked, add peppers and season with onion powder. Turn regularly until turkey is no longer pink.
Add zucchini, lemon juice, garlic, oregano and chicken stock and cook for an additional 3 to 4 minutes or until vegetables are tender but not overcooked. Remove from heat. Add parsley and serve.

Per Serving: 372 Calories; 18g Fat; 37g Protein; 17g Carbohydrate

Turkey Breast with Glazed Roasted Vegetables

1 1/2	pound turkey breast with skin
2	cups broccoli blanched and diced
2	cups celery root diced
4	cups green peppers diced
1/2	cup Walden Farms Balsamic Vinaigrette Dressing
2	tablespoons olive oil
1	teaspoon lemon pepper seasoning
1	teaspoon paprika

Heat oven to 325 degrees. Place breast, skin side up, in shallow open pan and brush lightly with oil. Roast 1 hour. Remove from oven. Place pepper, celery and broccoli around turkey. Continue roasting for 15 minutes. Meanwhile, stir together dressing and paprika. Remove turkey from oven. Brush with dressing. Continue roasting for an additional 15 minutes or until chicken is cooked. Fifteen minutes before cooking is complete, stir vegetables to glaze with pan juices.

When breast is done, let stand 10 minutes before carving. Remove vegetables from pan with slotted spoon, keep warm and serve alongside the turkey. Pan juices may be spooned over the sliced meat and/or served in a small dish.

Per Serving: 362 Calories; 18g Fat; 36g Protein; 14g Carbohydrate

Poultry

Turkey Casserole
Mediterranean Style

Turkey Dijonnaise style

1 1/2	pounds	turkey tenderloin
4	cups	leek sliced
4	cups	lettuce, iceberg julienne
4		basil leaves fried
1	tablespoon	Walden Farms Mayonnaise

1	tablespoon	Walden Farms Dijon Mustard Dressing
1	teaspoon	Dijon mustard
1 1/2	tablespoons	olive oil
		sea salt to taste
		pepper to taste

Mix mustard, dressing and mayonnaise and baste turkey.
Cook turkey in a 375-degree oven for 20 minutes or until cooked.
Slowly sauté leek in olive oil. When tender, add iceberg lettuce and cook for an additional minute. Season with salt and pepper.

Per Serving: 374 Calories; 17g Fat; 39g Protein; 14g Carbohydrate

....

Curry Turkey

1 1/2	pounds	turkey breast
1	cup	chicken stock
2	cups	celery root cubed 1/2" thick
2	cups	green peppers cubed 1/2" thick
1 1/2	cups	green onions sliced thick
2	cups	red onions finely sliced
2		limes
2		cloves garlic
1	tablespoon	ginger finely chopped

4	tablespoons	Walden Farms Orange Spread chopped
1	tablespoon	olive oil
1		jalapeno peppers seeded and sliced
2	teaspoons	curry powder
		sea salt to taste
		pepper to taste

Preheat oven to 400 degrees.

Combine jalapeño peppers, ginger, curry, garlic, salt and pepper in a blender or food processor. Blend, adding just enough olive oil to form a fine paste.

Rub paste mixture on turkey and put in a roasting pan. Add celery and peppers. Bake, uncovered, for 1 hour. Remove turkey from pan and discard fat and juices that have accumulated. Reduce oven to 325 degrees.
In a small bowl, combine the spread, two limes and chicken stock. Return turkey to pan. Pour orange, lime and chicken stock mixture over turkey. Add vegetables. Cover pan with foil and return to oven for 20 to 30 minutes.
Remove turkey from oven. Drain excess fat and retain the pan juices. In a saucepan, reheat with the green onions. Pour into a gravy boat and serve.
Garnish meat with raw red onion slices.

Per Serving: 364 Calories; 15g Fat; 37g Protein; 21g Carbohydrate

Poultry

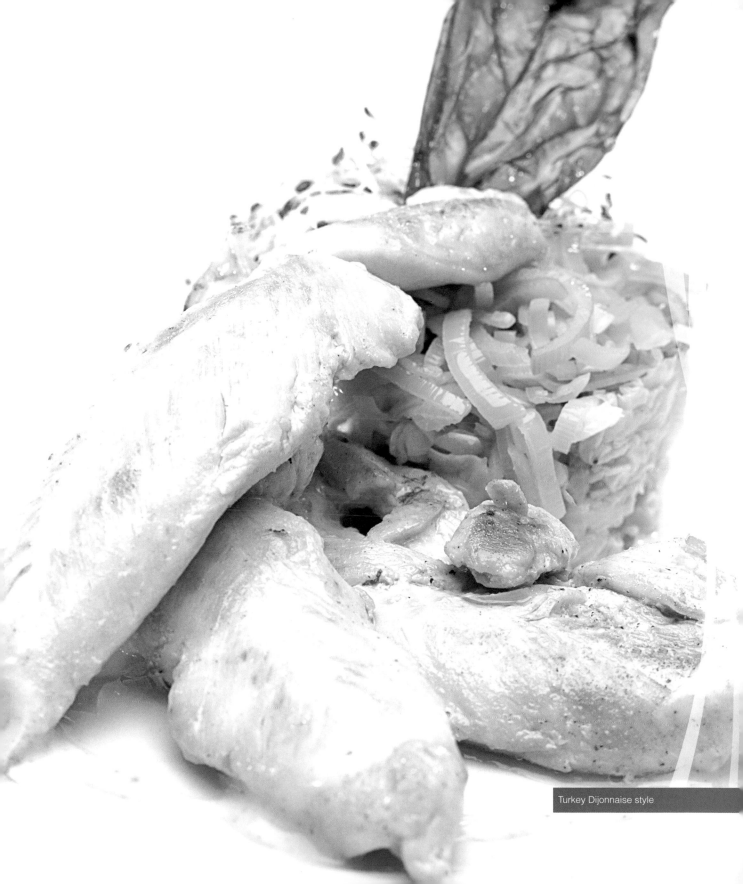

Turkey Dijonnaise style

Turkey Marmjte

1 1/2	pounds	turkey breasts
1/4	pound	ham
4	cups	chicken broth fat free
4	cups	zucchini green, sliced
2	cups	celery cubed
2	cups	broccoli chopped
2	teaspoons	thyme leaves chopped fine
1	cup	Walden Farms Tomato and Basil Sauce
2	teaspoons	paprika
1/2	teaspoon	pepper
1/2	teaspoon	sage
1	tablespoon	cumin

In a slow cooker, combine turkey, ham, broth, celery, sauce and seasoning. Cover and cook on HIGH for 4 hours. Add broccoli and cook, covered for an additional 30 minutes or until all vegetables are tender.
Sauté zucchini in 1 teaspoon of olive oil. Add just before serving.

Per Serving: 377 Calories; 16g Fat; 47g Protein; 11g Carbohydrate

....

Turkey Gratin with Cauliflower Purée

1 1/2	pounds	turkey breast cooked
8	cups	cauliflower
6	tablespoons	Walden Farms Alfredo Sauce
1	tablespoon	olive oil
2	tablespoon	curry paste
		sea salt to taste
		pepper to taste

Roll turkey in ½ of curry paste.
Cook cauliflower in boiling water for 10 to 12 minutes or until tender. Drain and purée in blender. Add remaining curry paste, half of the Alfredo sauce, salt and pepper to taste.

In an oiled gratin dish, arrange one layer of the cauliflower purée. Top with turkey. Coat with remaining purée. Drizzle with Alfredo sauce. Broil until browned.

Per Serving: 355 Calories; 17g Fat; 39g Protein; 13g Carbohydrate

Turkey Marmite

Turkey en Papillote with Vegetables

1 1/2	pounds turkey breast		3	tablespoons olive oil
4	cups broccoli		3	teaspoons Dijon mustard
2	cups zucchini diced		1	tablespoon mustard powder
2	cups mushrooms sliced 1/4" thick			sea salt to taste
1	teaspoon thyme leaves			pepper to taste
1	cup Walden Farms Tomato and Basil Sauce			

Sauté zucchini in olive oil. Season and set aside.
Sauté mushrooms in same pan. Set aside.
Season the turkey and baste with mustard.
Cut aluminum foil into a 12" square. Add turkey, zucchini, mushrooms and Tomato and Basil sauce. Sprinkle with thyme and drizzle with olive oil. Salt and pepper to taste. Close the foil to a hermetic square.
Bake in oven for 30 minutes at 375 degrees or until turkey is cooked and still juicy.
Dissolve mustard powder in 4 cups of water. Bring to a boil and add salt. Cook the broccoli in this liquid.
Serve the turkey and vegetables with the broccoli.

Per Serving: 375 Calories; 22g Fat; 38g Protein; 8g Carbohydrate

Braised Turkey with Tomato, Basil and Orange Sauce

2	pounds turkey breast boneless and skinless cubed trim excess fat		1	cup Ideal Protein Tomato Basil Soup prepared
1	tablespoon olive oil		1 1/2	tablespoons Walden Farms Orange Spread chopped
2	cups green onions			
4	cups asparagus		2	teaspoons cider vinegar
2	cups green peppers		1	teaspoon cumin seeds
2	teaspoons garlic crushed			sea salt to taste
1	teaspoon thyme			pepper to taste

Sear turkey in pan. Transfer to crock-pot.
In same pan, sauté green onions and green peppers. Transfer to crock-pot.
Brown cumin seeds in turkey pan. Add 1/2 cup of water to dissolve browns. Reduce.
Add 1 tablespoon of orange spread. Add tomato soup, thyme, garlic and seasoning.
Transfer to crock pot and cook on LOW for 6 hours.
Blanch asparagus in salted, boiling water. Serve asparagus with turkey and vegetables.

Per Serving: 353 Calories; 5g Fat; 60g Protein; 15g Carbohydrate

Turkey en Papillote with Vegetables

Turkey Skewers
with Mushrooms

1 1/2	pounds	turkey breast cubed 1/2"
3	cups	mushrooms
5	cups	portobello mushrooms
1	tablespoon	fresh herbs chopped fine
2 1/2	tablespoons	Walden Farms Blueberry Spread chopped
1	tablespoon	olive oil
6-8		rosemary stems

Mix blueberry spread with olive oil and herbs. Add the remaining ingredients.
Prepare skewers, alternating turkey with mushrooms. Salt and pepper.
Bake at 400 degrees or on a grill.

Per Serving: 356 Calories; 16g Fat; 41g Protein; 16g Carbohydrate

Turkey Meatballs

1 1/2	pounds	ground turkey
2	slices	smoked ham chopped
1/2	cup	beef stock
1	packet	Ideal Protein Salt and Vinegar Ridges crushed
1		egg white
6	cups	green peppers sliced
1 1/2	cups	green onions chopped fine
1	clove	garlic crushed
2	tablespoons	parsley chopped
3	tablespoons	Walden Farms Hickory Dressing
2	teaspoons	olive oil
		sea salt to taste
		pepper to taste

Cook green onions and garlic in olive oil for 5 minutes.
In a bowl, combine green onion, garlic, turkey, egg white, Ridges and dressing.
Salt and pepper.
Prepare 1" meatballs and cook in skillet. Remove excess oil. Add beef stock. Sprinkle with parsley. Reduce for 15 to 20 minutes, uncovered, until the meatballs are well cooked.
Sauté peppers in olive oil. Add garlic. Season.

Per Serving: 394 Calories; 18g Fat; 37g Protein; 21g Carbohydrate

Poultry

Turkey Skewers
with Mushrooms

Three-Meat Terrine

1/2	pound	turkey breast ground
1/4	pound	ground beef extra lean
1/2	pound	pork loin ground
4		hard-boiled eggs
2		egg whites
1/2	packet	Ideal Protein Salt and Vinegar Ridges crushed
4	cups	zucchini sliced lengthwise
4	cups	spinach chopped fine
1	teaspoon	pepper
1	clove	garlic minced
3	tablespoons	parsley chopped fine
1	package	onion soup mix
1	tablespoon	vegetable oil
1	teaspoon	dried basil
1	teaspoon	dried rosemary
1	teaspoon	fennel seeds
		bread mold

In a large bowl, mix all ground meats.
Blanch zucchini in salted, boiling water. Cool.
In a skillet, heat oil over medium heat and cook onion and garlic until tender.
Add spinach, basil, rosemary and fennel seeds. Mix and cook for an additional minute.
Transfer to bowl of ground meat. Pepper. Add onion soup mix, parsley, 2 egg whites and Ridges.

Preheat oven to 350 degrees.

Cover oiled bread mold with zucchini slices. Add half the meat mixture. Top with 4 hard-boiled eggs, sliced lengthwise. Cover with the other half of meat mixture and press gently. Cover mold with aluminum foil and place on an oven-safe dish. Add water to dish until it reaches half the height of mold. Bake in the oven for 75 minutes. The temperature inside the meat should be 165 degrees. Remove mold from oven and remove aluminum foil. Set aside for 30 minutes.
Degrease, cover with aluminum foil and refrigerate over night.
You may also serve this recipe hot.

Per Serving: 390 Calories; 21g Fat; 37g Protein; 14g Carbohydrate

Oriental Meatballs

1	pound	turkey breast ground
6	cups	soybean sprouts
1 1/2	cups	green onions
1/2	cup	green onions sliced
1	teaspoon	ginger ground
1	cup	Walden Farms Raspberry Spread chopped
2	tablespoons	Walden Farms Ketchup
1	tablespoon	olive oil
1	teaspoon	sesame oil
2	tablespoons	white vinegar
1	teaspoon	sesame seeds
		sea salt to taste
		pepper to taste

Combine turkey, 1/2 cup of green onions, ginger, salt and pepper. Shape into 12 meatballs.
Cook in a 375-degree oven for 35 minutes or until liquid runs clear. Remove fat
from pan.

Dissolve brown pieces in the bottom of the pan with 1 cup of water.
In a pot, combine spread, ketchup and vinegar. Boil until reduced by half. Add liquid from
oven pan drippings. Simmer for 10 minutes. Add meatballs and reheat.
Sauté onion and sprouts in sesame oil. Add roasted sesame seeds.

Per Serving: 351 Calories; 19g Fat; 37g Protein; 14g Carbohydrate

Turkey Teriyaki

1 1/2	pounds turkey breast 4 pieces
4	cups soybean sprouts
2	cups green peppers
2	cups green onions
2	teaspoons lemon juice
2	teaspoons garlic
2	teaspoons ginger chopped fine
1/4	cup Walden Farms Sesame Ginger Dressing
1	tablespoon sesame oil
1	clove garlic minced

Combine lemon juice, dressing and sesame oil. Use 1/2 to marinade turkey, (30 minutes to 2 hours). Set aside.
Barbeque or broil cutlets (4 to 6 minutes per side) brushing often with reserved marinade.
Sauté ginger and garlic in olive oil. Add peppers and onions. Cook for 3 minutes.
Add soybean sprouts and reserved marinade and sauté 5 minutes
Serve turkey on soybean sprouts.

Per Serving: 398 Calories; 19g Fat; 44g Protein; 17g Carbohydrate

....

Turkey Meatloaf

1 1/2	pounds turkey breast ground
3	egg whites
1/2	package Ideal Protein Salt and Vinegar Ridges crushed
2	cups celery chopped
4	cups cauliflower
2	cups spinach
1/2	jar Walden Farms Apple Butter Fruit Spread chopped
1	tablespoon olive oil
2	teaspoons poultry seasoning
	sea salt to taste

Cook celery in warm olive oil. Add spinach and cook until water is evaporated.
Allow to cool.
Mix cooked vegetable with ground turkey, fruit spread, seasoning, egg whites and Ridges. Form mixture into a loaf. Bake in a 350-degree oven for approximately 1 hour.
During this time, cook cauliflower in salted, boiling water until tender.
Serve a slice of meatloaf with the cauliflower on the side.

Per Serving: 352 Calories; 15g Fat; 41g Protein; 10g Carbohydrate

Poultry

Turkey Teriyaki

Rabbit Leg with Cauliflower Curry Purée

1 1/2	pounds rabbits legs
8	cups cauliflower
2	teaspoons parsley chopped
1	tablespoon Walden Farms Alfredo Sauce
1	tablespoon olive oil
3	tablespoons curry paste

Cook cauliflower in salted, boiling water. Drain. Add curry paste and Alfredo sauce. Purée in blender until smooth. Add chopped parsley.

Sauté rabbit legs in olive oil. Baste with curry paste and Alfredo sauce. Finish cooking in oven at 375 degrees for 30 minutes, basting with its fat (inside temperature should be 165 degrees).

Serve beside the purée.

Per Serving: 375 Calories; 19g Fat; 39g Protein; 12g Carbohydrate

Quail and Cauliflower Manchurian Style

12	quail breast skinless
2	egg whites wisked
1	tablespoon Ideal Protein Salt and Vinegar Ridges crushed
2	pounds cauliflower blanched
2	teaspoon garlic paste
2	teaspoons soy sauce
1 1/2	tablespoons sesame oil
1	teaspoon pepper
	sea salt to taste

Dip cauliflower florets in egg whites. Coat pieces with Ridges, salt, pepper, and ½ of garlic paste. Place in oven-safe dish and bake in a 400-degree oven for 5 to 10 minutes until brown.

In skillet, heat 1 tablespoon oil over medium heat. Add remaining garlic paste. Fry for one minute. Add soy sauce and 1/2 cup water. Mix well. Add the cauliflower florets. Cover. Cook until all liquid is absorbed.

Sauté seasoned quail breasts in sesame oil for 2 minutes on each side. Add soy sauce. Finish cooking slowly.

Serve with cauliflower.

Per Serving: 361 Calories; 12g Fat; 48g Protein; 16g Carbohydrate

Meat

Tips and tricks

All recipes provide for 4 servings.

Walden Farms Fruit spreads need to be chopped before mixing into any recipe in order to have the right consistency.

All the liquid quantities are a suggested minimum. You may increase the quantity in any recipe if you are a sauce-lover.

Wooden skewers must be placed in cold water overnight prior to use in order to avoid burning during the cooking process.

Blanching is an easy technique used to keep vegetables crisp and tender.
Vegetables are placed in salted, boiling water, just until the water returns to a boil.
Than placed into cold water to stop the cooking process.
Blanching ensures that the flavor and the nutritional value of the vegetable is preserved.

All Ideal Protein foods with the exception of the Ridges/Puffs should be prepared according to the preparation instructions on each package.

You may substitute ground beef in any recipe with Ideal Protein's Soy Patty.

If the meat selection indicated in any recipe is not available at your local butcher shop, you may substitute it with any other lean cut of meat.

Hey, any questions?
Find us on Chef Verati facebook page
or write chefverati@idealprotein.com

Bon appétit!

Beef Skewers with
Horseradish Sauce p.149

Spicy Honey Beef on Salad

1 1/2	pounds beef tenderloin lean, cubed
4	cups lettuce leaves
2	cups asparagus blanched
2	cups cucumber sliced
1	jalapeño pepper chopped
2	tablespoons herbs
2	tablespoons Walden Farms Honey Dijon Dressing
4	tablespoons Walden Farms Honey BBQ Sauce
1	tablespoon steak spice
2	tablespoons olive oil
	sea salt to taste
	pepper to taste
	skewers

Mix cucumber and asparagus with dressing.
Prepare a bed of lettuce leaves. Top with cucumber and asparagus.
Drizzle with dressing.

Put the beef cubes on skewers season and baste with olive oil and grill
at very high temperature.
Serve salad with beef skewers

Per Serving: 356 Calories; 18g Fat; 39g Protein; 6g Carbohydrate

....

Beef with Chinese cabbage

1 1/3	pounds ground beef extra lean,	1/2	bunch coriander chopped fine
6	cups Chinese cabbage finely sliced	6	tablespoons soy sauce
2	cups green peppers cut into" pieces	2	teaspoons olive oil
1	teaspoon Walden Farms		sea salt to taste
	BBQ Thick 'N Spicy Sauce		cayenne pepper to taste
2	cloves garlic minced		

Heat the Wok before adding the oil and bring up to high heat. Add ground beef and cook
for 5 minutes. Drain excess fat and set meat aside.

Add peppers to Wok and cook for a few minutes then add garlic. Add cabbage and cook
until tender. Season with soy sauce, salt and cayenne pepper.

Add BBQ sauce. Simmer for 1 minute. Top with coriander.

Per Serving: 356 Calories; 21g Fat; 32g Protein; 10g Carbohydrate

Spicy Honey Beef on Salad

Asian Beef with Raspberry Sauce

1 1/3	pounds beef tenderloin		1	clove garlic minced
2	cups bok choy 1/2-inch thick		1/2	cup Walden Farms Raspberry
3	cups soybean sprouts			Spread chopped
3	cups green onions		1	tablespoon sesame oil
1/2	teaspoon ground ginger		1/3	cup soy sauce

Thinly slice beef against the grain into bite-size strips. Set aside.

In a shallow dish, combine soy sauce, sesame oil, 1/2 of the raspberry spread, ginger and garlic. Mix well. Add beef strips, cover and refrigerate for 1 hour. Stir once during refrigeration. Remove meat from marinade and discard marinade.

Heat oil in a skillet over medium heat, add meat and cook until brown. Remove meat. Add onions, bok choy and bean sprouts to skillet and cook until tender and crisp. Add remaining raspberry spread. Cook for 5 minutes, stirring often or until hot.

> **NOTE: You can use pre-sliced fondue meat in this recipe.**

Per Serving: 364 Calories; 17g Fat; 42g Protein; 14g Carbohydrate

---

Beef Alsace Style

1 3/4	pounds beef shoulder cut 1" thick
4	cups sauerkraut
4	cups cabbage finely sliced
1	tablespoon Walden Farms Apple Butter
1/4	cup Walden Farms Sweet Onion Dressing
1	tablespoon onion powder

Season meat and brown under broiler.
Blanch cabbage for 1 minute in salted, boiling water.
Alternate layers of meat, sauerkraut, cabbage, onion powder and apple butter in slow cooker.

Add sweet onion dressing and 1 cup of water. Cook on LOW for 8 to 10 hours.

Per Serving: 353 Calories; 13g Fat; 44g Protein; 16g Carbohydrate

Beef and Garlic Lemon Kabobs

1 1/4	pounds beef tenderloin cut into 24 cubes	1	tablespoon oregano fresh
4	cups green peppers cut into 24 pieces	2	tablespoons olive oil
4	cups zucchini cut into 24 pieces	1/2	teaspoon sea salt
2	lemons cut into 6 wedges than halved	1/4	teaspoon pepper
12	cloves garlic unpeeled and crushed	6	12" metal skewers

Trim excess fat from beef.
Combine oil and oregano in small bowl. Add lemon pieces and unpeeled garlic cloves.
Pour over vegetables and mix well. Refrigerate for 2 hours.

Thread beef pieces on metal skewers alternating with vegetables and lemon.
Place kabobs on grid over medium heat. Grill 10 to 15 minutes for rare to medium, turning
occasionally. Season.

Per Serving: 354 Calories; 17g Fat; 34g Protein; 20g Carbohydrate

....

Veal Papillote with Citrus fruit

1 1/2	pounds veal cutlets 4 pieces	2	tablespoons olive oil
8	cups asparagus chopped		nutmeg ground
1	lemon juiced		sea salt to taste
1	tablespoon Walden Farms Orange Spread chopped		pepper to taste

Preheat oven to 400 degree.
"Butterfly" meat (so it opens like a book)

Mix orange spread, pepper, salt and nutmeg and spoon into meat. Top with lemon juice
and close opening. Oil on both sides.

Lay on 12" aluminum squares and top with lemon zests. Close papillote airtight and bake
in oven for 20 minutes.

Cook asparagus in salted boiling water.
Open the papillote and plate the meat.
Roll asparagus in meat drippings and serve.

Per Serving: 369 Calories; 19g Fat; 39g Protein; 14g Carbohydrate

Beef, Ham and Spinach Burgers

1	pound	ground beef extra lean
3	ounces	ham slices extra lean julienned
1		egg white
4		Portobello mushroom caps
2	cups	soybean sprouts
2	cups	celery root
2	cups	frozen spinach well drained and pressed
1/3	cup	Walden Farms Basil and Tomato Sauce
1	teaspoon	olive oil
1	teaspoon	Italian seasoning
1	teaspoon	red pepper flakes
		sea salt to taste
		pepper to taste

In a large bowl, combine beef, ham, spinach, garlic, Italian seasoning, pepper, egg white and salt. Mix with fingers until fully blended.

Prepare 4, 1" thick patties and grill on barbecue for about 6 minutes or until cooked.

Baste celery root and Portobello caps with olive oil and grill slowly.
Heat Basil and Tomato sauce to simmer.

Place burgers on grilled celery root. Top with Basil and Tomato sauce and sautéed sprouts, finish with Portobello caps.

Per Serving: 360 Calories; 19g Fat; 36g Protein; 15g Carbohydrate

Beef Goulash

1 1/3	pounds blade roast cubed
4	endives
4	cups mushrooms sliced
1	tablespoon Walden Farms Alfredo Sauce
2	tablespoons Walden Farms Basil and Tomato Sauce
1	tablespoon olive oil
1	tablespoon onion powder
1	bay leaf
1/2	tablespoon paprika
	sea salt to taste
	pepper to taste

Heat oil in skillet and brown meat on all sides. Transfer meat to slow cooker.
Sauté mushrooms and onion powder in the same skillet for a few minutes. Add to slow cooker.

Remove excess fat from skillet (to be used to sauté endives). Add 4 tablespoons of water. Simmer. Add this liquid to the slow cooker.
Add all remaining ingredients directly to the slow cooker and stir. Cook for 7 to 9 hours on MEDIUM.

Cut endives in half (lengthwise) and remove core. Blanch for 2 minutes in salted, boiling water.

Just before serving, sauté in skillet fat.
Place a piece of endive on each plate,add meat and mushrooms. Spoon on sauce.

Per Serving: 358 Calories; 20g Fat; 35g Protein; 5g Carbohydrate

Beef with
Szechuan Vegetables

1 1/2	pounds flank steak cut into 2" strips
2	cups broccoli chopped
2	cups celery chopped
2	cups cauliflower chopped
2	cups green peppers chopped
1/2	teaspoon sesame oil
	sea salt to taste
	pepper to taste

MARINADE

1/2	teaspoon ginger minced
2	tablespoons Walden Farms Ketchup
2	tablespoons oyster sauce
1	tablespoon soy sauce
2	dried hot red peppers chopped

Slice beef into 2" strips cut against the grain and at an angle.
Combine all ingredients for marinade in a medium bowl and add beef strips. Mix well and set aside for 30 minutes.

Cook vegetables in salted, boiling water. Remove from heat and cool vegetables in cold water. Drain well.

Heat oil in wok over medium heat. Remove beef from marinade (do not discard) add to wok, stir-frying until lightly browned. Remove with slotted spoon, draining well over wok. Set aside.

Remove 3/4 of oil from wok. On high heat, add vegetables and stir-fry for 15 seconds. Add 2 tablespoons of marinade. Bring to a boil. Return beef to wok and stir-fry until sauce thickens slightly.
Serve hot.

Per Serving: 362 Calories; 19g Fat; 36g Protein; 12g Carbohydrate

Veal and Vegetable Casserole

1 1/2	pounds ground veal			parsley (garnish)
4	cups beef stock		20	ounces Walden Farms
3	cups celery root diced 1/2"			Basil and Tomato Sauce
3	cups green peppers diced 1/2"		1	tablespoon olive oil
2	cups cauliflower diced 1/2"		1/2	teaspoon dried thyme
1	clove garlic minced			sea salt to taste
1/2	cup green onions chopped fine			pepper to taste

In a skillet, heat oil on medium heat and cook green onions, veal and garlic for 4 to 5 minutes or until meat is browned. Add stock and thyme. Bring to boil, cover partially and simmer for 30 minutes on low heat.

Add vegetables. Season. Cook for another 20 to 30 minutes on low heat until vegetables are cooked.

Per Serving: 359 Calories; 16g Fat; 37g Protein; 15g Carbohydrate

Breaded Beef with Leek

1	pound beef flank thinly sliced
2	egg whites wisked
6	cups leek sliced fine
2	cups green onions
1	packet Ideal Protein Salt and Vinegar Ridges crushed
1	tablespoon olive oil
	sea salt to taste
	pepper to taste

Dip beef into wisked egg whites one at a time, then into crushed Ridges ensuring each piece is well coated.

Heat oil in a large frying pan. Fry cutlets until well browned on both sides. Drain excess oil on paper towel.

In remaining olive oil, slowly cook leek and green onions covered. You may add water, if necessary. Cook for approximately 30 minutes or until tender.

Per Serving: 375 Calories; 17g Fat; 31g Protein; 26g Carbohydrate

Breaded Beef with Leek

Beef Skewers with Horseradish Sauce

1 1/3	pounds ground beef extra lean
1	packet Ideal Protein Barbecue Ridges crushed
6	cups celery root cubed 2" thick
2	cups green onions chopped fine
1	tablespoon garlic chopped fine
3	tablespoons parsley chopped fine
1/4	cup Walden Farms Alfredo Sauce
3	tablespoons horseradish
2	tablespoons Dijon mustard
	sea salt to taste
	pepper to taste

In a bowl, mix half of the horseradish, parsley, garlic, green onions, mustard and ground beef. Add Ridges and season. Prepare mixture into four kebabs and refrigerate for 1 hour.

Cook celery root in salted boiling water. Drain and add the other half of horseradish. Cook on stovetop for an additional 2 minutes. Puree celery root with Alfredo sauce and seasoning until consistency is creamy.

Place kebabs on skewers (or rosemary stems, or lemongrass stems) and grill on a very hot barbecue or pan.
Serve on celery root purée.

Per Serving: 355 Calories; 19g Fat; 31g Protein; 13g Carbohydrate

Braised Spiced Beef in Basil and Tomato Sauce

1 1/2	pounds	beef shoulder cubed 1" thick
6	cups	cabbage sliced
2	cups	broccoli
6	cloves	garlic
1	teaspoon	lemon juice
3	ounces	Walden Farms Basil and Tomato Sauce
2	tablespoons	olive oil
1	teaspoon	cider vinegar
1	teaspoon	allspice
1/2		cinnamon stick
		sea salt to taste
		pepper to taste

Heat 1 teaspoon of olive oil in large frying pan. Brown meat. Remove excess fat. Transfer to slow cooker.

Pour vinegar into frying pan to loosen pan drippings. Add water, reduce and add to meat along with the Basil & Tomato sauce.

Place cinnamon stick, garlic and ½ teaspoon of allspice to the slow cooker and cover. Cook on LOW for 8 to 10 hours, or until very tender.

Sauté cabbage in 1 teaspoon of olive oil in a pan and cook on low heat until tender. Add water, allspice, seasoning covered for an additional hour.

Cook broccoli in salted, boiling water.
Serve the cooked beef on a bed of cabbage and garnish with broccoli.

Per Serving: 363 Calories; 18g Fat; 38g Protein; 14g Carbohydrate

Braised Chili Flank Steak

1 1/3	pounds flank steak	2	teaspoons olive oil
4	cups bok choy quartered	2	tablespoons cider vinegar
4	cups green peppers chopped	2	teaspoons chili powder
1	chili pepper seeded	2	teaspoons onion
1 1/2	tablespoons Walden Farms Basil and Tomato Sauce		sea salt to taste
			pepper to taste

Score steak and rub with chili powder. Season.
Pound steak on both sides with a wooden mallet (or the edge of a knife) to tenderize. Cut into 6 pieces.

Brown steak in hot oil in a large skillet. Remove and set aside.
Sauté peppers in pan drippings. Add Basil and Tomato sauce. Add remaining salt and pepper to taste. Remove from heat.

Transfer steak and sautéed vegetables to slow cooker. Add hot chili peppers, cover and cook on LOW for 8 hours or until meat is tender.
Blanch bok choy in salted, boiling water. Add to cooker and leave to simmer with the meat for the last hour.

Per Serving: 351 Calories; 19g Fat; 32g Protein; 14g Carbohydrate

Slowly Braised Beef

1 1/2	pounds beef round steak	1/2	cup Walden Farms BBQ Sauce
4	cups green peppers sliced	2	teaspoons hot sauce
2	cups celery stalks diced	1	teaspoon onion powder
2	cups celery root diced		sea salt to taste
3	cloves garlic minced		pepper to taste
1/4	cup Walden Farms Basil and Tomato Sauce		

Cut beef into serving-sized portions. Brown beef in a bit of olive oil. Set aside.
Sauté vegetables in same pan.

Place vegetables on bottom of slow cooker. Top with beef and sprinkle with fresh ground pepper, minced garlic and onion powder.
Mix the BBQ and hot sauce in a small bowl with water. Add Basil and Tomato Sauce. Pour over the meat. Turn the slow cooker to LOW, cover and cook for 7 to 9 hours.

Per Serving: 351 Calories; 12g Fat; 41g Protein; 15g Carbohydrate

Korean Steak

1 1/2	pounds beef tenderloin, lean		1 1/2	tablespoons sesame oil
3	cups mushroom whole		1	tablespoon cider vinegar
2	cups asparagus blanched		1	tablespoon soy sauce
3	cups green onions sliced			sea salt to taste
1	tablespoon garlic crushed			pepper to taste
2	tablespoons Walden Farms Fruit Spread chopped			

Combine, green onion, garlic, fruit spread, vinegar and soy sauce.
Add beef tenderloin and marinate in the refrigerator overnight.

Grill steaks to desired doneness. Grill vegetables for a few minutes.

Remove green onions from the marinade. Cook slowly in a pan, draining any fat.
Serve the cooked green onions on top of the steaks. Arrange grilled vegetables on
the side.

Per Serving: 360 Calories; 17g Fat; 41g Protein; 12g Carbohydrate

Chinese Steak

1 3/4	pounds beef tenderloin, lean sliced 1/8" thick		6	tablespoons soy sauce
6	cups Chinese cabbage		1	tablespoon Chinese 5-spice powder
2	cups green onions			sea salt to taste
1	tablespoon sesame oil			pepper to taste
1	tablespoon cider vinegar			

Marinate beef in a mixture of vinegar, soy sauce and 1 tablespoon of water for 1 hour.

Sauté meat in very hot sesame oil. Remove and set aside.
In the same pan, add green onions and cabbage. Cook until cabbage becomes tender.
Add 1/2 of the marinade and reduce until syrup-like consistency. Add meat and stir well.

Per Serving: 374 Calories; 17g Fat; 46g Protein; 8g Carbohydrate

Korean Steak

Flank Steak with Garlic Soy Sauce

1 1/2	pounds flank steak
6	cups Chinese cabbage sliced 1/4" thick
2	cups red cabbage sliced 1/4" thick
1	tablespoon olive oil
8	tablespoons soy sauce
4	cloves garlic crushed
	sea salt to taste
	pepper to taste

Score flank steak on both sides.
Marinate the meat in soy sauce and garlic in the refrigerator for 24 hours.

Heat olive oil in a pan and slowly cook the Chinese cabbage. When tender, add half of the meat marinade, cover and simmer for 30 minutes. Add water if there is not enough liquid.
Repeat process in a different pan for the red cabbage.
Heat the broiler.

Remove meat from the marinade and place in an oven-safe dish under a pre-heated broiler for 8 minutes on each side. Cooking times vary, depending on the desired doneness.

Allow the meat to sit for 5 minutes. Slice at an angle and serve with the 2 different cabbages.

> **NOTE: You can boil some of the marinade for 5 minutes and use it to decorate the plates.**

Per Serving: 379 Calories; 21g Fat; 37g Protein; 9g Carbohydrate

Sesame-Ginger Beef Steak

1 1/3	pounds flank steak well trimmed		1	tablespoon cider vinegar
7 1/2	cups green peppers halved lengthwise		2	tablespoons soy sauce
2	tablespoons garlic crushed			sea salt to taste
2	tablespoons ginger grated			pepper to taste
2	teaspoons sesame oil			

Combine sesame oil, soy sauce, vinegar, ginger and garlic. Reserve 1 tablespoon of marinade. Combine marinade and beef flank steak in a plastic bag turning to coat. Close bag securely and refrigerate 6 to 8 hours (or overnight, if desired), turning occasionally. Remove steak from marinade. Set marinade aside.
Baste peppers with reserved marinade.

Place steak and bell pepper halves on grid over medium heat. Grill 12 to 15 minutes for rare to medium and until peppers are tender, turning steak and pepper halves once. Brush steak with reserved marinade before turning.

Carve steak diagonally against the grain into thin slices. Serve with peppers.

Per Serving: 383 Calories; 19g Fat; 33g Protein; 22g Carbohydrate; 6g Dietary Fiber

....

Roast Beef in Jelly Aspic Style

1 1/4	pounds beef tenderloin lean, roasted and julienned		1	teaspoon garlic cloves chopped
1 1/2	cups beef broth		1/2	cup minced parsley
1	envelope unflavored gelatin		4	tablespoons Walden Farms Dressing (your choice)
6	cups lettuce leaves		1	teaspoon Worcestershire sauce
1/2	cup celery root cubed		1/2	teaspoon Tabasco sauce
1/2	cup pickles sliced			sea salt to taste
1/2	cup green onions minced			pepper to taste

Cook celery root in salted water, drain well.
In a large bowl, mix gelatin and 1/2 cup of beef broth. Bring remaining cup of broth to a boil. Add to gelatin mixture and stir until gelatin is completely dissolved.
Take 2 tablespoons of this gelatin to put in the cold mold.
Arrange pickles in bottom of a terrine or cake mold. Carefully sprinkle beef over pickles. Let set in fridge.

Add remaining ingredients to the rest of the gelatin. Mix well. Chill until mixture has the consistency of unbeaten egg whites. Pour over pickles and meat in mold. Chill until firm. Unmold to serve. Place lettuce leaves on plates. Drizzle with dressing. Top with beef slices.

NOTE: To give the dish an incredible taste, flavor the beef broth with fresh herbs.

Per Serving: 353 Calories; 10g Fat; 38g Protein; 26g Carbohydrate

Sesame-Ginger Beef Steak

Beef Stew
Bourguignon Style

1 1/3	pounds beef shoulder cubed 1" thick
3	cups mushrooms
3	cups green peppers shredded
2	cups celery root cubed
1	tablespoon oregano crushed
2	tablespoons Walden Farms Basil and Tomato Sauce
7	ounces Walden Farms Hickory Smoked BBQ Sauce
2	teaspoons Worcestershire sauce
1 1/2	tablespoons olive oil
1 1/2	tablespoons onion powder
	sea salt to taste
	pepper to taste

In skillet, brown meat in hot oil. Drain excess fat. Transfer meat to slow cooker.

Sauté peppers, mushrooms and celery root. Add onion powder. Add to slow cooker.
Pour the Basil and Tomato sauce into the skillet. Once boiling, add to slow cooker.
Add BBQ sauce, oregano and Worcestershire sauce directly to slow cooker and cover.
Cook on LOW for 10 to 12 hours.

Remove 1/3 of the vegetables from the slow cooker and purée. Put the purée into a large skillet and add the sauce from the slow cooker. The sauce should coat the back of the spoon to be the right consistency.

Add the rest of the vegetables and meat to the skillet, stir well and serve.

Per Serving: 350 Calories; 15g Fat; 33g Protein; 15g Carbohydrate

Roast Beef with Mustard Celery Root Purée

1 1/4	pounds beef tenderloin lean		2	tablespoons Dijon mustard
2	ounces radish sprouts			sea salt to taste
8	cups celery root cubed			pepper to taste
1/2	cup Walden Farms Alfredo Sauce			
3	tablespoons olive oil			

Season beef. Sear in hot olive oil. Bake in a 400-degree oven for 40 minutes – or until desired doneness. Remove from pan and keep warm for 15 minutes.
Cook celery root in salted, boiling water. Drain. Purée. Add mustard, 1 tablespoon olive oil and Alfredo sauce. The purée should be light and creamy.

Garnish with radish sprouts.

Per Serving: 354 Calories; 21g Fat; 33g Protein; 10g Carbohydrate

Easy Beef and Sauerkraut Stew Bavarian Style

1 1/3	pounds flank steak sliced 1/2" thick		1	cup cider vinegar
6	cups sauerkraut		1	teaspoon caraway seeds
2	cups green onions			sea salt to taste
2	teaspoons olive oil			pepper to taste

Sear beef in olive oil. Remove and drain excess fat.
Add vinegar to the same pan and reduce liquid by half. Add half of the sauerkraut, caraway seeds, salt and pepper. Add beef slices. Add water to cover meat. Cover with remaining sauerkraut and caraway.
Bring to a boil then simmer, covered for 1 hour on very low heat.

> **NOTE: Ensure you use sauerkraut that is not marinated in white wine and that has zero carbohydrates.**

Per Serving: 373 Calories; 18g Fat; 33g Protein; 22g Carbohydrate

Roast Beef with Mustard Celery
Root Purée

Meat Loaf

1	pound ground beef extra lean		1/4	cup Walden Farms Ketchup
3	egg whites		1	teaspoon dry mustard
3/4	packet Ideal Protein Southwest Cheese Curls		1	teaspoon horseradish optional
4	cups green peppers chopped		1	tablespoon onion powder
2	cups fennel chopped			sea salt to taste
2	cups green onions chopped			pepper to taste

Preheat oven to 400 degrees.

Sauté green pepper. Add fennel and green onions. Cook for 5 minutes. Season and let cool.

Mix all ingredients well and shape into a loaf. Place on foil-lined baking pan, bake until brown and cooked inside

NOTE: This delicious meatloaf can be served hot or cold on a salad.

Per Serving: 355 Calories; 20g Fat; 27g Protein; 18g Carbohydrate

---

Beef and Vegetable Chili

1 1/4	pounds ground beef extra lean		2	teaspoons olive oil
2	cups celery root cubed		2	teaspoons onion powder
2	cups cauliflower blanched		2	teaspoons chili powder
2	cups green pepper cubed		2	teaspoons sea salt
2	cups mushrooms		1	teaspoon pepper
2	teaspoons garlic minced			
2	packets Ideal Protein Chili prepared			

In a pan, brown beef. Drain fat. Add chili powder, garlic and seasoning. Add chili sauce, celery root, green peppers and mushrooms. Transfer to a slow cooker. Cook on LOW for 8 hours. Blanch cauliflower in salted, boiling water and add to slow cooker for the last hour.

Per Serving: 356 Calories; 22g Fat; 28g Protein; 14g Carbohydrate

Beef and Vegetable Chili

Chili Blueberry Beef

1 1/2	pounds beef tenderloin, lean cubed
1	package Ideal Protein Chicken Soup prepared
4	cups celery root
4	cups spinach
1/2	teaspoon chili pepper finely chopped
1	teaspoon fresh ginger finely chopped
1	clove garlic crushed
5	ounces Walden Farms Blueberry Spread chopped
2	tablespoons olive oil
2	teaspoons cider vinegar
1	tablespoon soy sauce
	sea salt to taste
	pepper to taste

Sauté beef in hot oil. Add garlic, ginger, chili and cook for 1 minute - do not let it brown. Add blueberry spread and vinegar. Reduce. Add soy sauce and chicken soup and beef. If there is not enough liquid, add water. The sauce should coat the meat.

Cover and cook slowly, simmering on the stove or in the oven for 2 hours (you may also use a slow cooker). When meat is tender, remove and set aside, covered.

Cook celery root in salted, boiling water. Drain. Purée.
Sauté spinach in 1 teaspoon of olive oil and add to purée mixing well.

Make a "well" with vegetables and serve beef and sauce in the middle.

Per Serving: 372 Calories; 19g Fat; 43g Protein; 7g Carbohydrate

Beef Burritos with Green Salsa

1 1/4	pounds ground beef extra lean
1	packet Ideal Protein Pancakes prepared (4)
3	cups spinach
2 1/2	cups green onion
2	tablespoons jalapeño
2	tablespoons lime juice
1	cup Walden Farms Chipotle Dressing
2	cups green peppers chopped
1/2	teaspoon ground cumin
1 1/2	tablespoons chili powder
	sea salt to taste
	pepper to taste

In large skillet, brown ground beef over medium heat for 8 to 10 minutes or until meat is no longer pink, stirring occasionally. Drain excess fat.

Season beef with chili powder, cumin, salt and pepper. Stir in spinach and cook until soft. Remove from heat and stir in dressing.

To serve, spoon approximately 1/4 of the beef mixture in the center of each pancake. Fold bottom edge up over filling. Fold sides to center, overlapping edges.

Serve with salsa mix – chopped green pepper, lime juice, jalapeño peppers, green onions, salt and pepper.

Per Serving: 360 Calories; 18g Fat; 34g Protein; 16g Carbohydrate

Honey-Mustard Burgers
with Asparagus

1 1/2	pounds	ground beef extra lean
48		asparagus
2	cups	lettuce leaves
2	cups	green onions sliced
4	tablespoons	Walden Farms Honey Dijon Dressing
1	teaspoon	dried oregano
1/4	teaspoon	black pepper coarsely ground
		sea salt to taste
		pepper to taste

Combine ground beef, 2 tablespoons honey-mustard dressing, 1 teaspoon oregano, green onions and pepper, mixing lightly but thoroughly. Divide beef mixture into 4, 1/2-inch thick patties, 4" in diameter.

Heat large heavy nonstick skillet over medium heat for 5 minutes. Pan-broil patties 7 to 8 minutes, turning once.

Blanch asparagus in salted, boiling water.
Plate the lettuce leaves, drizzle with dressing, Top with hamburger and garnish side with asparagus and dressing.

Per Serving: 386 Calories; 21g Fat; 37g Protein; 13g Carbohydrate

Korean Barbecued Beef

1 1/2	pounds beef tenderloin lean cubed
2	cups Chinese cabbage sliced
4	cups daikon julienned
2	cups green onions sliced
2	tablespoons Walden Farms Thick 'N Spicy BBQ Sauce
1	teaspoon sesame oil
1	cup soy sauce
1	teaspoon tamari sauce
1/4	teaspoon pepper
1	teaspoon Chinese 5-spice powder
4-6	skewers prepared

Mix soy sauce, BBQ sauce, sesame oil, pepper and beef cubes in a heavy, sealed plastic bag. Chill for 2 to 4 hours turning bag occasionally.

Meanwhile soak wooden skewers in water for 30 minutes.

Drain meat, reserving the marinade for broiling. Thread meat cubes onto each skewer.

In sesame oil, cook the green onions. Add the cabbage and cook slowly for 10 minutes. Add the daikon, Chinese 5-spice and tamari sauce. Remove from stove. Place skewers on rack and broil 3 to 4" from the heat for 12 to 14 minutes or until done, turning once and brushing with reserved marinade.

Arrange skewers on a serving plate along with vegetables.

Per Serving: 355 Calories; 14g Fat; 43g Protein; 15g Carbohydrate

Szechwan Beef Stir-Fry

1 1/3	pounds flank steak well-trimmed
2	cups soybean sprouts
4	cups green peppers cut into 1-inch pieces
4	cloves garlic crushed
1	tablespoon ginger minced
1	teaspoon Walden Farms Fruit Spread chopped
1	tablespoon sesame oil
2	tablespoons soy sauce
1/4	teaspoon red pepper flakes
	sea salt to taste
	pepper to taste

Cut steak in half, lengthwise; cut each half against the grain into 1/8-inch thick strips. Combine sesame oil, soy sauce and fruit spread. Pour over beef strips, tossing to coat.

Heat sesame oil in wok or large nonstick skillet over medium-high heat. Add peppers, garlic and ginger. Cook 30 seconds. Add soybean sprouts and stir-fry 30 seconds. Remove vegetables from pan. Set aside.

Stir-fry beef strips (half at a time) for 2 to 3 minutes. Return vegetables and beef to pan and heat through. Serve immediately.

Per Serving: 387 Calories; 21g Fat; 35g Protein; 16g Carbohydrate

Basil and Tomato Mushroom Meatballs

MEATBALLS

1 1/3	pounds	ground beef extra lean
1		egg white
4	cups	green peppers roasted and skinned
1	ounce	chicken stock
1	teaspoon	oregano
1	teaspoon	olive oil
1/2	teaspoon	garlic powder
		sea salt to taste
		pepper to taste

SAUCE

1	ounce	ham julienned
4	cups	mushrooms sliced
1	clove	garlic minced
1/4	cup	parsley chopped
1/2	teaspoon	oregano
1/2	cup	Walden Farms Basil and Tomato Sauce
2	teaspoons	onion powder
		sea salt to taste
		pepper to taste

Mix together all meatball ingredients.

Shape meat into golf ball-sized balls. Sauté in oil until golden brown.

Prepare the sauce. Sauté mushrooms in the fat from the meat. Add ham, onion powder and garlic. Drain the fat. Add Basil and Tomato sauce. Simmer in covered saucepan on low heat for 1 hour stirring often. If the sauce is too thick, add water. If sauce is too thin, cook uncovered for 15 minutes.

Add browned meatballs and simmer for an additional 30 minutes.

Coat green pepper halves with the olive oil used for cooking the meat. Roast in a 375 degree oven until soft. Remove the skin and slice. Use as a bed for the meatballs.

NOTE: To simplify skin removal, after the peppers are roasted, put them into a sealed plastic bag for a few minutes. The steam will help the skin to be easily removed.

Per Serving: 351 Calories; 13g Fat; 38g Protein; 15g Carbohydrate

Meatballs in Mushroom Sauce

1 1/4	pounds ground beef extra lean, minced	1	cup oyster mushrooms
1/2	packet Ideal Protein BBQ Ridges crushed	2	cups green onions sliced
2	packets Ideal Protein Mushroom Soup prepared	1	teaspoon olive oil
4	cups mushrooms		sea salt to taste
1	cup enoki mushrooms		pepper to taste

Preheat oven to 450 degrees.

In bowl, mix beef, Ridges and 1/2 cup of mushroom soup. Shape mixture into approx. 32 meatballs and place on greased oven-safe dish. Cook for 8 minutes, or until cooked. Drain all fat.

Prepare sauce by sautéing mushrooms in olive oil. Add green onions, remaining mushroom soup and season.

Serve meatballs with mushroom sauce.

Per Serving: 368 Calories; 19g Fat; 39g Protein; 10g Carbohydrate

Basil and Tomato Veal Scallops

2	pounds veal sirloin thinly sliced
8	cups broccoli
1	clove garlic peeled
2	cups Walden Farms Basil and Tomato Sauce
4	tablespoons olive oil
	sea salt to taste
	pepper to taste

Cook broccoli in salted, boiling water.
Heat 2 tablespoons of olive oil with garlic for 5 minutes. Remove garlic and set aside.

Heat 2 tablespoons of olive oil in skillet at medium-high heat. Add Basil and Tomato sauce. Cook veal for 3 to 4 minutes on each side. Serve with broccoli. Drizzle with garlic olive oil and season.

Per Serving: 419 Calories; 27g Fat; 37g Protein; 8g Carbohydrate

Meatballs in Mushroom Sauce

Beef and Bok Choy Stir-fry

1 1/3	pounds	flank steak cut in 3" thin strips
3	cups	bok choy chopped
2	cups	bamboo shoots canned sliced
1	cup	green pepper sliced
2	cups	celery chopped
3	tablespoons	green onions finely chopped
4	tablespoons	fresh ginger thinly sliced
3		cloves garlic thinly sliced
1		tablespoon Walden Farms Fruit Spread chopped
3		teaspoons sesame oil
1		tablespoon soy sauce

Marinate sliced steak for 30 minutes in 1 teaspoon oil, 1 tablespoon soy sauce, fruit spread and 1 tablespoon of ginger.
Separate the leaves from the bock choy. Blanch in salted, boiling water. Cool and cut into 1.5" pieces.

Brown garlic in 2 teaspoons of oil over medium heat. Remove beef from marinade and sauté until brown. Add bamboo, bok choy, celery, green onions and fry for a few minutes. Add marinade and boil until reduced.

Per Serving: 353 Calories; 20g Fat; 33g Protein; 12g Carbohydrate

....

Sauté Veal Liver with Green Onion Compote

2	pounds veal liver sliced		1		tablespoon olive oil
4	cups celery root cut into 1/2" thick sticks				sea salt to taste
4	cups green onions slices				pepper to taste
2	teaspoons Walden Farms Apple Spread chopped				

Cook celery root in salted, boiling water.
Slowly cook green onions in 1/2 teaspoon of olive oil until tender. Add apple spread and simmer for 2 minutes.
In 1/2 teaspoon of olive oil, sauté veal liver, 2 minutes on each side, until inside is pink (cut to check).
Sauté celery in 1/2 teaspoon of olive oil until golden.
Plate. Top with green onion compote and serve celery root on the side.

Per Serving: 384 Calories; 14g Fat; 43g Protein; 22g Carbohydrate

Beff and Bok Choy Stir-fry

Stuffed Veal Cutlets

1	pound veal cutlet 4 pieces, boneless
1	cup ground veal chopped
1	cup broccoli
3	cups celery root cubed 1/2"
2	tablespoons olive oil
12	mushrooms chopped
1/2	cup green onions chopped
1	tablespoon parsley chopped fine
1/4	cup Walden Farms Basil and Tomato Sauce
	sea salt to taste
	pepper to taste
	Butcher String

In a skillet, heat oil on medium heat. Add mushrooms, shallots and parsley, cook for 3 minutes. Add ground veal, cook on low heat for 4 to 5 minutes. Add Basil and Tomato sauce and mix well. Cook for 3 to 4 minutes on medium heat until sauce is reduced. Season. Mix ingredients in a blender until smooth. Set aside to cool.
(Make sure this mixture is not too liquid).

Preheat oven to 350 degrees.

Pound cutlets until thin. Distribute filling in veal cutlets and roll, securing with string.

In a clean skillet, heat remaining oil on medium heat and sauté veal rolls on each side for 2 to 3 minutes. Transfer into oven-save dish. Add celery root. Cover with aluminum foil and bake in oven for 10 to 12 minutes.

Per Serving: 357 Calories; 19g Fat; 37g Protein; 10g Carbohydrate

Veal Rolls with Ham

1	pound veal steaks 4 pieces cut very thin
1/2	pound ham finely chopped
1	packet Ideal Protein Apple and Cinnamon Puffs crushed
1	egg white
8	cups cauliflower
2	teaspoons lemon zest
2	tablespoons parsley finely chopped
1	tablespoon sage finely chopped
2	cups Walden Farms Basil and Tomato Sauce
2	tablespoons vegetable oil
	sea salt to taste
	pepper to taste

In a bowl, mix 3/4 Puffs, ham, lemon zest, parsley, sage, salt, pepper and egg white.
Spread 3/4 of the mixture on veal steaks and roll up. Hold together with wooden toothpicks.

In a skillet, heat vegetable oil and cook meat rolls for 4 to 5 minutes. Transfer to serving dish and keep warm.

Heat 3/4 of the Basil and Tomato sauce and pour over meat rolls.
Cook cauliflower in salted water. Transfer to baking dish. Add remaining ¼ Basil and Tomato sauce. Top with last 1/4 Puffs. Bake in 400 degree oven for 5 minutes.

Per Serving: 350 Calories; 18g Fat; 32g Protein; 13g Carbohydrate

Barbecue Honey and Ginger Pork Loin

2	pounds pork loin
1	cup chicken broth
4	cups bok choy cut in 1" pieces
4	cups bean sprouts
3	teaspoons fresh ginger finely chopped
1	tablespoon Walden Farms Honey BBQ Sauce
3	tablespoons sesame oil
3	tablespoons oyster sauce
3	tablespoons soy sauce
	sea salt to taste
	pepper to taste

Combine BBQ sauce, oyster sauce, soy sauce, chicken broth, pepper and ginger in a bowl. Mix well. Place pork loins and marinade in a sealed plastic bag and refrigerate for 8 hours or overnight.

Remove loins from marinade, set marinade aside.
Grill pork loins over medium-high temperature for 15 to 25 minutes, turning often and basting with marinade.

Sauté bok choy in oil for a few minutes. Once tender, add bean sprouts and remaining marinade. Continue cooking for 1 minute. Remove from skillet.
Reduce liquid to one spoon and return vegetables to skillet coating with reduced liquid.

Slice pork thinly and arrange on a serving platter. Garnish with fresh parsley.

Per Serving: 353 Calories; 19g Fat; 35g Protein; 10g Carbohydrate

Barbecue Pork Loin Roast

2	pounds pork loin
2	cups celery root cut 1/2" thick
3	cups green peppers sliced 1/2-inch thick
3	cups Portobello mushrooms sliced 1/2-inch thick
1	cup Walden Farms Basil and Tomato Sauce
1/2	cup Walden Farms Ketchup
4	tablespoons Walden Farms Caramel Spread
2	tablespoons olive oil
1/2	cup cider vinegar
1	teaspoon chili powder
	sea salt to taste
	pepper to taste

Season meat on all sides and place in a 375-degree oven until cooked. Remove from roasting pan and set aside in a warm place.

Season vegetables and drizzle with olive oil. Bake in oven with roast. Cook until tender and slightly brown, stirring regularly.

Drain fat. Add caramel spread and vinegar. Reduce. Add ketchup and Basil and Tomato sauce. Add chili powder. Simmer for 10 minutes. Add water if consistency is too thick. Adjust seasoning to taste

Per Serving: 356 Calories; 16g Fat; 34g Protein; 19g Carbohydrate

Barbecue Style Pork Chops

2	pounds pork loin chops cut in 4 pieces, no fat
4	endives
4	tablespoons Walden Farms Hickory Smoked BBQ Sauce
1	tablespoon olive oil
1/2	cup cider vinegar
4	tablespoons dry mustard
	sea salt to taste
	pepper to taste

Sear pork chops in olive oil. Arrange in an oven-safe baking dish.

Combine 4 tablespoons of water, vinegar and dry mustard and mix well. Pour over chops. Cover and bake at 400 degrees for 30 minutes.

Blanch the endives, cut lengthwise into two pieces, add to the baking dish and coat with sauce. Cook for another 30 minutes until meat and endives are tender.

> **NOTE: If the sauce is too liquid, reduce in a pan until it reaches a syrupy consistency. If too thick, add water.**

Per Serving: 350 Calories, 13g Fat; 36g Protein; 20g Carbohydrate

Pork Roast with Sauerkraut

1 1/2	pounds pork roast
7	cups sauerkraut fresh or in a jar
1	cup green onions quartered
1	tablespoon Walden Farms Apple Spread chopped
1/2	tablespoon olive oil
	sea salt to taste
	pepper to taste

Season meat.
Sear roast on all sides in 1 tablespoon of olive oil.
Drain and rinse the sauerkraut, season to taste. Add apple spread and green onions. Cover the roast with this mixture.

Preheat oven initially to 400 degrees and place the roast covered in center of oven. Bake for about 2 hours at 350 degrees or until pork is cooked.

Per Serving: 353 Calories; 18g Fat; 30g Protein; 19g Carbohydrate

Ham and Leek Rolls

1 1/2	pounds ham sliced	1	teaspoon thyme branch
1/8	packet Ideal Protein Salt and Vinegar Ridges crushed	1	teaspoon olive oil
3	cups leek chopped		sea salt to taste
2	cups green peppers chopped		pepper to taste
3	cups spinach		

In olive oil, slowly cook leek and green peppers with thyme and garlic powder until soft and tender. Add spinach, cook 1 minute.

Put the cooked vegetables on slices of ham and roll up. Place in a greased baking pan. Drizzle with olive oil and sprinkle Ridges. Bake in a 375-degree oven until very hot.

Serve on a bed of spinach or lettuce

Per Serving: 392 Calories; 20g Fat; 33g Protein; 21g Carbohydrate

Ham and Pork Burgers

1 1/2	pounds pork loin chopped	2	tablespoons Walden Farms Alfredo Sauce
1/2	pound ham extra lean chopped		
1	tablespoon Ideal Protein Apple and Cinnamon Puffs crushed	1	tablespoon olive oil
1	egg	1	teaspoon cumin
5	cups celery root cubed		sea salt to taste
3	cups watercress		pepper to taste

Mix ham, pork, Alfredo sauce, egg, Puffs and pepper in a blender until the mixture is finely ground.

Form 4 patties and grill for 6 to 7 minutes.

Coat celery root cubes with olive oil, salt, pepper and cumin. Roast in a 375 degree oven for approximately 40 minutes (or until tender).

Blanch the watercress in salted, boiling water and cool in ice water.
Purée celery root with the watercress and season to taste.

Per Serving: 366 Calories; 14g Fat; 36g Protein; 7g Carbohydrate

Ham and Leek Rolls

Braised Pork on a Bed of Cabbage and Zucchini

1 2/3	pounds	pork chops
4	cups	zucchini cubed
4	cups	red cabbage shredded
1	cup	lemon juice
2 1/2	tablespoons	fresh ginger grated
2	tablespoons	Walden Farms Apple Spread chopped
2	tablespoons	Walden Farm Sesame Ginger Dressing
1	tablespoon	olive oil
		sea salt to taste
		pepper to taste

Remove all fat from the pork.

Slowly cook red cabbage in olive oil. Cover and add water if needed. After 30 minutes the cabbage should be tender.

Sear the seasoned pork chops in olive oil on both sides. Add them to the cabbage. Keep covered and finish braising the pork.

In the pork pan, sauté zucchini and ginger. When nice and tender, add the apple spread and boil for 1 minute. Add lemon juice.

Mix the ginger dressing with the red cabbage and juice from the zucchini.
Plate cabbage and place pork chop on the side. Garnish with zucchini.

Per Serving: 380 Calories; 22g Fat; 32g Protein; 15g Carbohydrate

Apricot Pork Loin on Sauerkraut

2	pounds	pork loin cut 1" thick
8	cups	sauerkraut without carbohydrates or alcohol
3	teaspoons	garlic crushed
1/4	cup	Walden Farms Apricot Spread chopped
1	teaspoon	soy sauce
2	teaspoons	Dijon mustard
1	ounce	olive oil
1 1/3	tablespoons	cider vinegar

Heat oil on medium-high temperature. Add pork. Cook for 4 to 5 minutes on each side, basting regularly with the fat. Set aside.

Mix apricot spread, cider vinegar, soy sauce and garlic. Add mixture to pan. Reduce slightly. Add pork and baste with sauce. Add mustard to the sauce at the last minute. Heat the sauerkraut.

Plate sliced pork on sauerkraut and top with sauce.

Per Serving: 352 Calories; 16g Fat; 33g Protein; 21g Carbohydrate

....

Mushroom Gratin with Prosciutto

1	pound	prosciutto sliced
8	ounces	ham cubed
8	cups	mushrooms sliced
1/2	teaspoon	garlic crushed
1/4	cup	Walden Farms Basil and Tomato Sauce
		sea salt to taste
		pepper to taste

Cook ham and prosciutto on medium-high temperature. Add mushrooms and cook until the mushrooms change color and become tender.
Add garlic and cook for another 1 to 2 minutes. Add Basil and Tomato sauce, mix well. Cook until Basil and Tomato sauce is absorbed. Place in a baking dish and brown under the broiler.

> **NOTE: Prosciutto on its own will salt the dish.**

Per Serving: 360 Calories; 16g Fat; 44g Protein

Apricot Pork Loin on Sauerkraut

Stuffed Apple Flavored Pork Loin

1	pound	pork loin
1/2	pound	ground pork
1 1/2	cups	chicken stock
1	packet	Ideal Protein Salt and Vinegar Ridges crushed
6	cups	red cabbage sliced
1	cup	green pepper chopped
1	cup	green onions finely chopped
2	tablespoons	parsley finely chopped
2	tablespoons	Walden Farms Apple Spread chopped
2	teaspoons	olive oil
	sea salt	to taste
	pepper	to taste

STUFFING MIXTURE
In a skillet, heat olive oil on medium heat and cook green onions with peppers for 4 minutes. Add ground pork. Mix well and cook on low heat for 5 minutes. Add apple spread. Cook for another 5 minutes. Add ridges and cook for 2 minutes.

Preheat oven to 350-degrees.
Cut pork loins lengthwise in half and garnish with mixture. Roll and attach with string.

In a skillet, heat olive oil at medium heat and sauté pork loins. Cook in oven for 25 to 30 minutes. Set aside in hot serving dish. Add remaining chicken stock.

Slowly cook red cabbage in olive oil. Add 1 cup of chicken stock. Cover and cook in the oven until cabbage is tender. Season.

Sprinkle with parsley.

Per Serving: 368 Calories; 20g Fat; 31g Protein; 16g Carbohydrate

Grilled Honey Pork Tenderloin with Peppers

2	pounds pork tenderloin		1/2	cup soy sauce
4	cups green peppers finely chopped		1/2	teaspoon ground cinnamon
2	cups green onions chopped fine			sea salt to taste
2	cups cabbage sliced			pepper to taste
2	cloves garlic crushed			Butcher String
4	tablespoons Walden Farms Honey BBQ Sauce			

Marinade: Mix BBQ sauce with soy sauce, garlic and cinnamon.
Sauté green peppers, green onions and cabbage in 1 teaspoon of olive oil.
Add 2 teaspoons of marinade. Reduce. Season. Set aside to cool.

Make a lengthwise incision in the tender loin. Stuff with sautéed vegetables. Close and tie well. Cover with marinade and set aside for 1 hour. Drain and put on hot grill. During cooking, baste with marinade and cook until the center of the tenderloin is cooked. The marinade will create a sweet crust.

> **NOTE: Do not overstuff the meat as it needs to close completely.**

Per Serving: 361 Calories; 8g Fat); 52g Protein; 19g Carbohydrate

---

Quick Stir-Fry

1 1/2	pounds pork tenderloin cut 1/4" thick		4	tablespoons ginger chopped
2	cups soybean sprouts washed		2	tablespoons Walden Farms Asian Salad Dressing
2	cups Chinese cabbage chopped		1	tablespoon Walden Farms BBQ Sauce
2	cups green peppers sliced 1/4" thick		1	tablespoon olive oil
1	cup radish sliced		2	teaspoons sesame oil
1	teaspoon hot red chili peppers chopped			sea salt, to taste
5	tablespoons green onions sliced			pepper, to taste
2	tablespoons garlic crushed			

Heat oil in skillet on medium-high heat. Add pork. When browned, add green pepper. Cook 5 minutes, stirring occasionally. Add soybean sprouts and cabbage. Add hot chili peppers, garlic and ginger. Stir-fry for 5 minutes on medium heat or until vegetables are crisp and tender. Add salad dressing and BBQ sauce. Add green onions and radish and cook an additional 2 minutes.

Per Serving: 355 Calories; 14g Fat; 43g Protein; 16g Carbohydrate

Stuffed Pork Chops

1 1/2	pounds	pork loin chops 4 pieces
3 /4	pound	lean pork shoulder ground
1/2	packet	Ideal Protein Apple and Cinnamon Puffs crushed
1	cup	chicken stock
4	cups	green pepper chopped
2	cups	green onions chopped fine
2	cups	chili peppers
2	teaspoons	minced garlic

STUFFING MIXTURE

1/2	teaspoon	sage finely chopped
1/2	teaspoon	thyme chopped
1/2	teaspoon	dry mustard
3 /4	teaspoon	garlic powder
1	teaspoon	onion powder
1	teaspoon	cayenne pepper ground
1/2	teaspoon	ground nutmeg
1/2	teaspoon	ground cumin
	sea salt	to taste
	pepper	to taste

In a small bowl, thoroughly combine the stuffing mixture ingredients. Set aside.
Prepare pork chops by trimming all the fat. Cut a large pocket (to the bone) into the larger side of each chop to hold the stuffing.

In a large skillet, brown ground pork in olive oil over high heat for about 3 minutes. Add onions, bell peppers, garlic and 2 tablespoons of the seasoning mix. Stir well. Cook for about 5 minutes, stirring occasionally and scraping pan bottom well. Cook until mixture is well browned, for 6 to 8 minutes, stirring occasionally. Add stock and cook for 5 minutes, stirring frequently. Stir in the Puffs and cook about 2 minutes more, stirring constantly. Remove from heat.

Sprinkle the remaining stuffing mixture evenly on both sides of the chops and inside the pockets, pressing it in by hand. Prop chops with pocket side up in an ungreased 13" x 9" baking pan. Spoon about 1/4 cup stuffing into each pocket. Set remaining stuffing aside. Bake chops with pockets up in a 400-degree oven until the meat is done, for about 20 minutes.

Reheat remaining stuffing in the oven in a small pan.
Serve immediately with each chop arranged on top of a portion of the remaining stuffing.

Per Serving: 369 Calories; 13g Fat; 35g Protein; 22g Carbohydrate

Pork Chops with Mushrooms

1 1/2	pounds pork chops 4 pieces	1	teaspoon olive oil
8	cups mushrooms chopped		sea salt to taste
1	teaspoon dill weed		pepper to taste
4	packets Ideal Protein Mushroom Soup prepared		

Remove all fat from pork.
Sauté seasoned pork and set aside.
In same pan, sauté mushrooms. Add dill seed.

Put half of mushrooms in a baking dish, add pork chops and top with other half of mushrooms. Coat with mushroom soup.

Bake in a 375 degree oven for 15 minutes or until the chops are cooked.

Per Serving: 399 Calories; 19g Fat; 47g Protein; 9g Carbohydrate

Cuban-Style Roast Pork with Zesty Mint Zucchini

2	pounds pork loin boneless	8	tablespoons mint leaves finely chopped
8	cups zucchini thinly sliced	2	tablespoons dried oregano
3 /4	cup lime juice	2	tablespoons olive oil
1	lemon		sea salt to taste
2 1/2	cup Walden Farms Orange Spread chopped		pepper to taste
3	tablespoons garlic		

Combine lime juice, lemon juice, orange spread, garlic, mint, oregano, olive oil, salt and pepper. Pour over roast. Cover and refrigerate overnight.

Place roast in pan, reserving marinade. Bake in preheated 400-degree oven for 55 minutes or until meat is cooked.

Once cooked, allow roast to sit for 10 minutes, cut into thin slices. Bring reserved marinade to a boil and pour over roast. Serve on top of zucchini.

Per Serving: 354 Calories; 15g Fat; 33g Protein; 17g Carbohydrate

Pork Chops with Mushrooms

Pork Meatballs
with Sweet-Sour Sauce

2	pounds	pork loin ground
1	packet	Ideal Protein Apple and Cinnamon Puffs crushed
1/2	cup	egg whites
6	cups	celery root 1" cubes
2	cups	green onions
4	tablespoons	Walden Farms Honey BBQ Sauce
4	teaspoons	Walden Farms Fruit Spread chopped
2	tablespoons	olive oil
4	tablespoons	cider vinegar
1	teaspoon	garlic powder
1	teaspoon	garlic salt
	sea salt to taste	
	pepper to taste	

Heat oven to 400 degrees.

Mix ground pork with Puffs, egg whites, garlic powder and garlic salt until well mixed. Shape into 1 1/2" balls (for ease in shaping meatballs, wet hands slightly). Bake in ungreased pan until brown, 15 to 20 minutes.

Sauté celery in olive oil. Season. Place in oven safe pan and stir regularly. When tender, remove from oven. Add sliced green onions. Stir well and keep warm until service.

When meatballs are cooked, remove from pan and set aside. Drain fat and bring 1 cup of water to a simmer to dissolve drippings.

In another pan, add fruit spread and vinegar. Bring to a boil until liquid is reduced by half. Add drippings (liquid from the meatball cooking pan). The sauce should coat a spoon. Simmer for 5 minutes.

Put meatballs into the sauce and reheat. Coat with sauce and serve with celery root.

Per Serving: 351 Calories; 15g Fat; 34g Protein; 12g Carbohydrate

Taco Pork Skillet

1 1/2	pounds pork tenderloin cut into strips	2	tablespoons Walden Farms
2	packets Ideal Protein Pancakes prepared		Zesty Italian Dressing
4	cups green peppers cut 1/2" thick	2	teaspoons olive oil
2	cups zucchini	1	ounce taco seasoning mix
2	cups watercress		sea salt to taste
			pepper to taste

Season pork with taco seasoning.
Heat olive oil in large skillet on medium-high heat. Add pork. Stir-fry for 2 minutes.
Add green peppers. After 2 minutes, add zucchini, 1/2 cup water and remaining
seasoning mix. Mix well and bring to a boil. Reduce heat to medium and cover.
Simmer for 5 minutes. Let stand for 5 minutes.

Spoon meat into Pancakes and wrap. Place on greased baking pan and bake in a
375 degree oven for 5 minutes until very hot.

Serve with watercress or any other green salad.

> **NOTE: A Mexican flavored dish that will please the whole family.**

Per Serving: 365 Calories; 9g Fat; 48g Protein; 22g Carbohydrate

---

Spicy Pork Stew

2	pounds pork loin cubed	2/3	teaspoon ginger
1/4	pound smoked ham	1	tablespoon oregano finely chopped
3	cups green peppers	1	teaspoon olive oil
1/2	cup okra cubed	3	tablespoons onion powder
2	cups turnip cubed	2/3	teaspoon turmeric
2	cups radish sprouts		sea salt to taste
2/3	teaspoon chili pepper		pepper to taste
1/2	cup garlic minced		

In a pan, heat olive oil. Brown meat. Remove meat from pan and drain excess fat. Add
peppers, chili pepper, turmeric, onion powder and garlic. Cook but do not brown. Add
okra and turnips. Add meat. Add oregano and 1 cup of water and cover. Simmer for 2 or
3 hours or until pork is tender. Add salt and pepper during the last half hour, if needed.
Serve meat and vegetables coated with the sauce and topped with radish sprouts.

> **NOTE: This dish is even better if you prepare it the day before and reheat it. If you
> like it spicy, add jalapeños.**

Per Serving: 361 Calories; 10g Fat; 33g Protein; 24g Carbohydrate

Taco Pork Skillet

Zucchini Gratin with Ham

1 1/3	pounds ham thinly sliced
8	cups zucchini sliced 1/2" thick
2	garlic bulbs
1	teaspoon rosemary chopped fine
1 1/2	tablespoons olive oil
	sea salt to taste
	pepper to taste

Roast garlic: Cut the top of the head of garlic and coat with 1 tablespoon of olive oil. Bake in a 375-degree oven for 40 minutes or until garlic is tender. Remove from shell and crush.

Sauté zucchini in olive oil. Drain well.
Layer a lightly greased baking dish with zucchini, overlapping the slices. Season and add rosemary and the garlic purée. Layer with ham, then with another layer of zucchini.

Drizzle with olive oil and broil until zucchini is cooked.

Per Serving: 386 Calories; 21g Fat; 31g Protein; 19g Carbohydrate

Ham Muffins

1 1/4	pounds ham extra lean chopped	2	tablespoons parsley finely chopped
4	eggs beaten	4	tablespoons Walden Farms Honey Dijon Mustard Dressing
1	package Ideal Protein Southwest Cheese Curls crushed	1	tablespoon Dijon mustard
7	cups greens (your choice for accompanying side salad)	1	tablespoon olive oil
1	celery stalk finely chopped		sea salt to taste
1/2	cup onion chopped		pepper to taste

Preheat oven to 350 degrees.
Mix all ingredients except olive oil in a bowl.
Grease muffin tin with olive oil. With a spoon, fill muffin tin (12 muffins)
Cook in oven for 30 minutes or until golden. Cool before removing from tin.

NOTE: These muffins will be a delight with fresh green salad.

Per Serving: 351 Calories; 16g Fat; 37g Protein; 9g Carbohydrate

Zucchini Gratin with Ham

Pork Stuffed Crepes

1 1/2	pounds	pork loin finely chopped
1	cup	shrimp canned
1		egg white beaten
2	packets	Ideal Protein Pancakes prepared (4 crepes)
1	cup	celery finely chopped
4	cups	bean sprouts washed and drained
3	cups	cabbage finely chopped
1	cup	green onions chopped fine
2	teaspoons	Walden Farms Apple Spread chopped
1	teaspoon	Walden Farms Ketchup
1	tablespoon	olive oil
1	teaspoon	Chinese Hot mustard
1/4	cup	soy sauce
		sea salt to taste
		pepper to taste

Heat wok. Add 1 tablespoon of oil and heat until hot but not smoking. Add pork, cook until light brown, about 3 minutes. Add bean sprouts, green onions, celery, cabbage, shrimp, soy sauce, apple spread and salt. Cook and stir 1 minute. Remove all ingredients from wok. Reduce liquid until syrupy. Cool mixture.

Brush pancake edges with egg whites.

Spoon 1/4 cup of the filling diagonally across the center of the pancakes. Bring lower point over filling. Fold over. Seal side. Bake in a 400-degree oven until crispy. Serve immediately on extra sprouts and cabbage

Serve with hot mustard and ketchup.

Per Serving: 388 Calories; 10g Fat; 35g Protein; 15g Carbohydrate

Lamb with Mushroom and Mustard Sauce

2	pounds	lamb
2	tablespoons	olive oil
4	cups	portobello mushrooms sliced
2	cups	mushrooms sliced
2	cups	green onions sliced
2	tablespoons	Walden Farms Basil and Tomato Sauce
2	tablespoons	Walden Farms Alfredo Sauce
2	tablespoons	Dijon mustard
1	teaspoon	green peppercorn
	sea salt	to taste
	pepper	to taste

Cut meat lengthwise. Season both sides.

In very hot oil, cook meat for 3 minutes on each side until lightly pink in the middle. Remove and keep warm. Drain excess fat from pan and add all mushrooms. Sauté on high heat until tender. Lower heat and add green peppercorns and green onions. Cook 2 minutes. Add 1/2 cup water. Reduce by 1/2. Add 2 sauces and cook until the mixture coats the back of a spoon.

Pour sauce into bottom of serving plate with pieces of mushroom. Top with lamb.

Per Serving: 350 Calories; 14g Fat; 38g Protein; 21g Carbohydrate

Minty Lamb Souvlaki

2	pounds lamb chops lean, cubed
4	cups cucumber cubed
1	lemon
2	cloves garlic crushed
2 1/2	tablespoons mint chopped fine
1	tablespoon olive oil
	sea salt to taste
	pepper to taste
	skewers prepared

SALAD
4	cups arugula
1	tablespoon olive oil
1	tablespoon fresh mint

Mix olive oil, lemon juice, ½ tablespoon mint, garlic and seasoning. Add lamb and refrigerate for 1 hour. Drain, alternate meat with cucumber on skewers.

Cook at high temperature for 6 to 8 minutes. Baste with marinade during cooking.

Sauté arugula for 1 minute in 1 tablespoon of olive oil. Add fresh mint and serve, topped with the meat.

Per Serving: 353 Calories; 18g Fat; 39g Protein; 6g Carbohydrate

Rack of Lamb

2 1/2	pounds lamb chops lean		1	tablespoon Walden Farms Basil
6	cups celery root cubed			and Tomato Sauce
2	cups broccolini			sea salt to taste
2	tablespoons rosemary			pepper to taste
3	heads garlic			

Rub meat with a mixture of salt, pepper and 1/2 tablespoon of rosemary. Sear on each side, fat side down first, in a warm dry pan. place in a 400 degree oven for 20 to 30 minutes. Set aside for 10 minutes.

Cook celery root in salted, boiling water with rosemary stem.
Roast garlic head in the pan used to cook the meat.
Purée celery root with the peeled roasted garlic and rosemary.

Drain fat from lamb. Return pan to stove and reheat. Add water and garlic. Reduce until dry. Add Basil and Tomato sauce and water. Simmer. Season. Strain.

Serve with celery root and broccolini cooked in salted water.

Per Serving: 368 Calories; 14g Fat; 49g Protein; 10g Carbohydrate

Indian Lamb Curry

2	pounds lamb chops, lean cubed		1	tablespoon Walden Farms Apple
6	cups celery root			Spread chopped
2	cups green onions		2	teaspoons olive oil
1	teaspoon garlic crushed		1	tablespoon curry paste
1	teaspoon thyme or 2 stems, if fresh			sea salt to taste
1	cup Walden Farms Basil			pepper to taste
	and Tomato Sauce			

Sear meat in pan than transfer to a slow cooker.
In the same pan, sauté green onions and celery root. Add curry paste and apple spread.
Transfer to slow cooker.

Add 1/2 cup of water to pan to dissolve drippings. Add Basil and Tomato sauce, thyme, garlic and seasoning. Cook on LOW for 6 hours.

Per Serving: 353 Calories; 15g Fat; 40g Protein; 11g Carbohydrate

Rack of Lamb

Rosemary Lamb Skewers

1 3/4	pounds	lamb chop, lean cubed
3	cups	green peppers cubed
3	cups	zucchini sliced 1" thick
2	cups	mushrooms
3	tablespoons	rosemary chopped fine
1	cup	Walden Farms Basil and Tomato Sauce
2	tablespoons	olive oil
		sea salt to taste
		pepper to taste
		skewers prepared

Mix Basil and Tomato sauce and rosemary. Marinate meat in 1/4 of this mixture in the refrigerator for 1 hour.

Prepare skewers with meat and vegetables. Season to taste.

Grill at high temperature.

To serve, coat with the rest of the marinade.

NOTE: Rosemary is an excellent way of giving lamb a rich flavor.

Per Serving: 354 Calories; 17g Fat; 36g Protein; 13g Carbohydrate

Satay Lamb with Cumin

2	pounds	lamb chops lean, sliced very fine
3	tablespoons	lemon juice
1	tablespoon	coriander powder
1	tablespoon	Dijon mustard
1	tablespoon	cumin powder to taste
		sea salt, to taste
		pepper

VEGETABLES

6	cups	green peppers sliced very fine
2	cups	green onions sliced very fine
2	tablespoons	lemon juice
1	tablespoon	coriander chopped fine
1	teaspoon	cumin powder
		skewers prepared

Preheat broiler.

Mix lamb with all ingredients.
Put on skewers. Grill for 3 minutes on each side or until meat is cooked.

VEGETABLES: Mix all ingredients and refrigerate for 2 hours.

Arrange a heap of raw, marinated vegetables on each plate. Top with skewers.

Per Serving: 357 Calories; 12g Fat; 41g Protein; 21g Carbohydrate

Fish and seafood

Tips and tricks

All recipes provide for 4 servings.

You may replace the fish selection in any recipe using a similar textured fish if you are unable to find the fish specified or if you simply do not like it. Also, feel free to use frozen fish, in some cases it may be easier to manipulate.

It's important not to overcook seafood as the texture becomes chewy and loses its entire flavor.

Celery Root, also known as Celeriac is not the root of the common celery.
It's actually grown for its root and not the leaves or stems. It is an excellent vegetable served cooked or raw.

Hey, any questions?
Find us on Chef Verati facebook page
or write chefverati@idealprotein.com

Bon appétit!

Asparagus and Marinated Swordfish
with Lemon Sauce p.225

Curry Mahi-Mahi Salad

2	pounds mahi-mahi cooked		2	tablespoons Walden Farms French Onion Dip	
1	cup celery minced		2	tablespoons Walden Farms Mayonnaise	
1	cup green onions		3/4	teaspoon curry paste	
1	cup green peppers		1	teaspoon curry powder	
1	cup radish			sea salt to taste	
4	cups spinach fresh			pepper to taste	
1	tablespoon lemon juice				

Mix celery, green onions, green pepper, radish and fish. Add dip, mayonnaise, lemon juice, curry paste and pepper. Mix well.
Place on a bed of fresh spinach. Sprinkle with curry powder.

NOTE: A nice way of turning a simple fish into a tasty salad rich in nutrients. You may use any leftover cooked fish in this recipe.

Per Serving: 370 Calories; 12g Fat; 55g Protein; 8g Carbohydrate

Mahi-Mahi and Vegetable Casserole

2	pounds mahi-mahi		1/2	cup Walden Farms Alfredo Sauce	
1	packet Ideal Protein Chicken Soup Mix prepared		1	teaspoon olive oil	
2	cups broccoli			sea salt to taste	
3	cups celery root cubed and blanched			pepper to taste	
3	cups mushrooms				

Season and sear fish. Add celery root and mushrooms to pan. Once tender, add soup and Alfredo sauce. Simmer until fish is cooked.

In salted boiling water, blanch broccoli. Add to casserole and simmer for another 5 minutes.

Per Serving: 374 Calories; 13g Fat; 56g Protein; 8g Carbohydrate

Curry Mahi-Mahi Salad

"Grilled" Glazed Mahi-Mahi Steaks with Chinese Cabbage

2	pounds mahi-mahi cut into 2" cubes	4	tablespoons Walden Farms Honey Dijon Dressing	
6	cups Chinese cabbage			
2	cups red cabbage	1	teaspoon olive oil	
3	tablespoons garlic crushed	3	tablespoons soy sauce	
2	tablespoons ginger finely chopped		sea salt to taste	
			pepper to taste	

Marinade fish in a mixture of soy sauce, ginger, 1 tablespoon of garlic and dressing. Refrigerate for a minimum of 2 hours.
Grill fish while basting with the marinade. Turn often.
Sauté Chinese and red cabbage in olive oil and 1 tablespoon of ginger until tender.
Serve fish on a bed of cabbage.

Per Serving: 388 Calories; 13g Fat; 56g Protein; 10g Carbohydrate

....

Mahi-Mahi Ratatouille

1 1/2	pounds mahi-mahi 4 pieces	1	tablespoon Walden Greens Tomato and Basil Sauce	
4	cups zucchini diced			
2	cups green peppers diced	2	tablespoons olive oil	
2	cups green onions chopped fine		paprika to taste	
2	cloves garlic chopped fine		sea salt to taste	
			pepper to taste	

Sauté zucchini. Remove from heat.
Sauté green onions, peppers and garlic. Add Tomato and Basil sauce and cook for a few minutes. Season with paprika, salt and pepper. Cook slowly until vegetables are AL DENTE.

Top ratatouille (mixture) with fish. Cover and cook in a 375 degree oven for 10 minutes or until fish is cooked.

Per Serving: 360 Calories; 15g Fat; 43g Protein; 12g Carbohydrate

Fish and seafood

Mahi-Mahi in Raspberry Sauce

1 1/2	pounds mahi-mahi 4 pieces cut 1" thick		4	tablespoons Walden Farms Raspberry Fruit Spread chopped
4	endives			
4	cups spinach		1	tablespoon olive oil
1	clove garlic crushed		1	teaspoon cumin
4	tablespoons Walden Farms Honey Dijon Dressing			sea salt to taste pepper to taste

Preheat barbecue to medium-high temperature.

Partially, blanch endives in salted, boiling water for 2 minutes.
Mix Honey Dijon dressing, oil, raspberry spread, cumin and garlic in a bowl.
Baste both sides of the fish and endives with the mixture setting aside 4 tablespoons to be used later.
Place fish on oiled grill. After a few minutes, add the endives. Turn once at half-time.
Turn endives after a few minutes.
Grill for 8 to 10 minutes or until the fish is opaque and can easily be removed with a fork.

Just before serving, combine the remaining 4 tablespoons of the dressing with the spinach. Place in the center of plate with one grilled endive. Top with mahi-mahi.

> **NOTE: This recipe can me made with sushi grade tuna and may be eaten raw.**
> **Remember: Tuna is a restricted food that may only be consumed once a week.**
>
> **You may also bake this recipe in a 375-degree oven.**

Per Serving: 372 Calories; 13g Fat; 47g Protein; 19g Carbohydrate

Mahi-Mahi with Broccoli in Ginger & Onion Sauce

2	pounds mahi-mahi	1	teaspoon sesame oil
6 1/2	cups broccoli florets	1	tablespoon soy sauce
1	cup green onions chopped		sea salt to taste
1	tablespoon fresh ginger finely chopped		pepper to taste
1/2	cup red onions sliced		
2	tablespoons Walden Farms Jersey Sweet Onion Dressing		

Blanch broccoli in salted, boiling water. Cool and drain.
Sauté fish in sesame oil until 75% cooked. Add ginger, green onions, soy sauce and dressing. Add 4 tablespoons of water. Complete cooking fish.
Add broccoli to sauce. Simmer for 2 minutes.

Per Serving: 390 Calories; 13g Fat; 57g Protein; 10g Carbohydrate

----

Mahi-Mahi Salad Bake

1 1/2	pounds mahi-mahi 4 pieces	1	packet Ideal Protein Salt and Vinegar Ridges crushed
2	cups celery sliced 1/4" thick		
2	cups leek sliced	1	teaspoon olive oil
2	cups asparagus		sea salt to taste
2	fennel bulbs sliced		pepper to taste
1	cup Ideal Protein Leek Soup prepared		

Preheat oven to 400 degrees. Prepare a greased baking dish.
Heat oil on low heat in pan and cook celery, leek and fennel. Add 1 cup of water and leek soup. Adjust seasoning if necessary. Bring to a boil and simmer for 4 minutes.
Cook asparagus in salted, boiling water.
Gently fold fish into the vegetable and soup mixture. When combined, spoon into baking dish and sprinkle with Ridges.
Bake 40 to 45 minutes or until fish is cooked.

Per Serving: 406 Calories; 11g Fat; 52g Protein; 24g Carbohydrate

Fish and seafood

Mahi-Mahi with Broccoli in Ginger & Onion Sauce

Mahi-Mahi Mediterranean Style

1 3/4	pounds	Mahi-mahi 4 pieces
4	cups	arugula
3	cups	zucchini sliced
1	cup	fennel bulbs
1	tablespoon	lemon juice retain skin for zest to garnish
1	tablespoon	parsley chopped fine
1	tablespoon	green onions chopped fine
1	tablespoon	savory chopped fine
1	tablespoon	oregano chopped fine
1	tablespoon	basil chopped fine
2	tablespoons	olive oil
		sea salt to taste
		pepper to taste

Sear mahi-mahi steaks on each side until just pink in the middle. Cover and set aside. Heat half of the oil in a skillet. Add fennel. When the fennel starts to soften, add green onions, lemon juice, chopped herbs and seasoning. Only add and sauté zucchini 3 minutes before serving.

In another pan, heat remaining olive oil and add arugula for one minute. Sprinkle with sea salt.

Make a bed of arugula on each plate. Top with fish steaks and vegetable mixture. Garnish with lemon zest.

NOTE: The fried arugula lends its crispy texture and bitter taste to this recipe.

Per Serving: 381 Calories; 17g Fat; 49g Protein; 8g Carbohydrate

Halibut Fillets with Spicy Sauce

2	pounds halibut fillets	1	cup Walden Farms
8	cups cauliflower		Alfredo Sauce
3	cloves garlic minced or pressed	1/2	teaspoon Tabasco sauce
1/2	cup parsley chopped fine		or Harissa
1/4	cup Walden Farms Ketchup	1 1/2	tablespoons olive oil
1/4	cup Walden Farms Original BBQ Sauce		sea salt to taste
			pepper to taste

Preheat oven to 425 degrees.
Cook cauliflower in salted, boiling water. Drain and pour into a oven-safe dish.
Drizzle with olive oil and coat with Alfredo sauce.
Combine ketchup, BBQ sauce, Tabasco, parsley and garlic. Season. Place fish in a separate oven-safe dish and top with sauce. Bake both dishes at the same time for 10 to 12 minutes or until fish easily flakes.
Garnish with parsley before serving.

NOTE: You can use any type of white fish for this recipe, depending on availability.

Per Serving: 351 Calories; 11g Fat; 52g Protein; 12g Carbohydrate

Indian Halibut Fillets

2	pounds halibut 4 pieces	1 1/2	teaspoons curry powder
8	cups broccoli	1	teaspoon curry paste
1	tablespoon Walden Farms Alfredo Sauce		sea salt to taste
1	tablespoon olive oil		pepper to taste
5	tablespoons Dijon mustard		

Preheat oven to 400 degrees.
Arrange fillets in a shallow oven-safe dish.

In a bowl, mix Alfredo sauce, mustard and curry powder. Add salt and pepper to taste.
Spread sauce evenly over fish. Bake in the oven for 12 to 15 minutes.
Cook broccoli in salted, boiling water.
Dissolve curry paste in olive oil and 2 tablespoons of broccoli water. Drizzle over broccoli just before serving.

NOTE: You may choose any Walden Farms Sauce you love.

Per Serving: 352 Calories; 11g Fat; 53g Protein; 9g Carbohydrate

Warm and Cold Marinated Halibut Salad with Ginger

1	pound	halibut fillets cut into fine strips
1	pound	halibut fillets cut into 4 pieces
4	cups	cucumber seeded and sliced
2	cups	celery shredded
2	cups	celery root shredded
4	lemons	juiced
1	tablespoon	fresh ginger finely grated
1	tablespoon	dill chopped
1	tablespoon	Walden Farms Bleu Cheese Dip
2	teaspoons	olive oil
2	teaspoons	cider vinegar
	sea salt	to taste
	pepper	to taste

Pour half of the lemon juice over the celery and celery root. Marinate for 1 hour.
Pour the remaining lemon juice, ginger and dill over the sliced halibut. Add olive oil.
Allow to marinate for at least 30 minutes.

Salt cucumber slices and allow to sit for 10 minutes. Rinse and pat dry with paper towels.
Mix cucumber and celery in a salad bowl with ginger and dill.
Whisk dip and vinegar. Salt and pepper to taste. Pour over the salad.

Season the 4 pieces of fish and slowly steam until perfectly cooked.
Arrange salad on plates with marinated fish and with cooked fish (the cooked fish can be served cold or hot).

> **NOTE: If just one kind of fish is preferred, steam or marinate all the fish.**
> **A refreshing and tasty salad - perfect for a hot summer day meal.**

Per Serving: 357 Calories; 8g Fat; 50g Protein; 14g Carbohydrate

Halibut Marengo Style

2	pounds	halibut steaks
4	cups	mushrooms cut in 4
2	cups	celery root small cubes
2	teaspoons	lemon juice
2	cups	green onions finely sliced
1	tablespoon	thyme finely chopped
2	tablespoons	parsley finely chopped
1	cup	Walden Farms Tomato and Basil Sauce
2	tablespoons	olive oil
		sea salt to taste
		pepper to taste

Sear halibut in olive oil. Remove from pan and set aside.
In the same pan, sauté mushrooms until brown. Add celery root and green onions, cook covered until tender. Add Tomato and Basil sauce. Add fish, cover and simmer for 8 minutes or until fish is cooked.
Remove from heat. Add parsley and thyme, cover and set aside for 10 minutes.
Adjust seasoning with salt, pepper and lemon juice if needed.
Serve the fish on a bed of vegetables and top with sauce.

> **NOTE: You may replace the Walden Farms Tomato and Basil Sauce with Ideal Protein's Tomato and Basil soup. Remember it will increase the nutritional facts accordingly.**

Per Serving: 356 Calories; 12g Fat; 50g Protein; 10g Carbohydrate

Halibut Royale

2	pounds	halibut steak's
1	packet	Ideal Protein Salt and Vinegar Ridges crushed
3	cups	spinach
3	cups	turnip
2	cups	green onions finely chopped
2	tablespoons	lemon juice
1	tablespoon	parsley chopped
1	cup	Walden Farms Mayonnaise
1 1/2	tablespoons	olive oil
		sea salt to taste
		pepper to taste

Combine water, lemon juice and salt. Add Halibut and marinate in refrigerator for at least 1 hour.

Drain marinated halibut and bread both sides with Ridges. Place in shallow, greased baking dish.

Combine half of the mayonnaise with green onions and coat fish. Sprinkle with paprika. Bake in a 450-degree oven for about 10 minutes or until halibut flakes when tested with a fork.

Cook turnip in salted, boiling water until tender. Purée. Add remaining mayonnaise and parsley. Adjust seasoning if needed.
Sauté spinach in olive oil.

TO PLATE: Make a circle with the spinach (bigger than the fish), add turnip purée in the middle and top with fish.

NOTE: Ideal Protein Salt and Vinegar Ridges will salt the fish. If you prefer, use Barbecue Ridges instead.

Per Serving: 383 Calories; 12g Fat; 54g Protein; 15g Carbohydrate

Halibut in Vine Leaves

2	pounds	halibut
24	large	vine leaves blanched
4	cups	mushrooms diced
2	cups	endives
2	teaspoons	lemon juice
1/4	cup	garlic finely diced
1/4	cup	fresh parsley finely chopped
1/4	cup	fresh basil finely chopped
1/4	cup	fresh chives finely chopped
2	tablespoons	olive oil
2	teaspoons	olive oil
2	tablespoons	soy sauce low carbohydrate content
	sea salt	to taste
	pepper	to taste

Sauté mushrooms in 2 tablespoons of olive oil. Add garlic, parsley, basil, chives and half of the soy sauce.

For each portion, arrange 4 leaves like a flower. Top each with mushrooms and place one piece of halibut on each flower.

Fold in corners of flower to cover the fish and mushrooms. Place on aluminum foil and make an airtight packet. Cook in oven for 15 minutes at 300 degrees.

Mix lemon juice, 2 teaspoons of olive oil and the other half of the soy sauce to make a salad dressing. Serve vine leaves on a bed of endives. Drizzle with dressing.

> **NOTE: An excellent dish you can prepare in advance!**
> **You may substitute vine leaves with blanched cabbage leaves instead.**

Per Serving: 372 Calories; 15g Fat; 50g Protein; 8g Carbohydrate

Asparagus and Marinated Swordfish with Lemon Sauce

1 1/2	pounds swordfish	3	tablespoons olive oil
8	cups asparagus		sea salt to taste
2	tablespoons lemon juice		pepper to taste
1 1/2	teaspoons Walden Farms Honey Dijon Dressing		

Slice swordfish very fine and marinate in lemon juice for 30 minutes. The lemon marinade will cook the fish. Drain. Set lemon juice aside.

Cook asparagus in salted, boiling water until tender and set aside on a warm plate. Top with swordfish.

Slightly warm olive oil and add lemon juice. Remove from heat. Add mustard dressing and whisk well. Serve immediately over fish.

Per Serving: 359 Calories; 17g Fat; 40g Protein; 13g Carbohydrate

Swordfish Sashimi with Tosa Joyu Vegetables

1	sheet nori	TOSA JOYU	
1 3/4	pounds swordfish	3	tablespoons soy sauce
4	cups soybean sprouts	5	teaspoons katsuobushi
2	cups zucchini sliced	1	tablespoon fish sauce
2	cups green peppers sliced	2 1/2	teaspoons wasabi
2	teaspoons sesame oil		

Cut fish into slices 1/2-inch thick and 6-7" long. (the length of the nori sheet)
Lay the nori flat on a hard surface. (The Japanese use a bamboo mat to facilitate rolling.) With the wide side of the mat facing towards you. Place a long slice of fish along the length of the nori and roll the nori into a long, thick, tight cylinder shape. Cut crosswise into 1 1/2-inch slices with a sharp knife. Roll and cut the remaining fish and nori in the same way. Serve with dipping sauce.

TOSA JOYU (SOY-BASED DIPPING SAUCE): Place all ingredients in a small saucepan. Bring to a boil, uncovered, stirring constantly. Remove from heat. Strain and set aside to cool. Divide into serving dishes and garnish with wasabi.
At the last minute, sauté the green pepper in oil. Add zucchini. When tender, add soybean sprouts. Season with sauce and serve.

Per Serving: 391 Calories; 16g Fat; 51g Protein; 16g Carbohydrate

Asparagus and Marinated
Swordfish with Lemon Sauce

Asiatic Style Swordfish

1 1/2	pounds swordfish steaks
2	cups zucchini sliced
2	cups asparagus blanched
2	cups green peppers cut in 1" pieces
2	cups soybean sprouts
2	teaspoons fresh ginger grated
1	tablespoon Walden Farms Caramel Dip
2	tablespoons olive oil
2	tablespoons cider vinegar
3	tablespoons soy sauce
1	teaspoon Chinese five-spice
	sea salt to taste
	pepper to taste

Mix zucchini and green peppers. Marinate in 1/2 of the olive oil with ginger and blanched asparagus in the refrigerator until ready to grill.

Mix caramel dip, vinegar, soy sauce and five spice. Baste both sides of the fish with this sauce.

In a non-stick pan, heat oil and brown fish for 5 minutes. Turn over. Add remaining sauce. Salt and pepper to taste.

Cook for another 5 minutes or until the fish is opaque and the sauce becomes like a syrup. Grill Vegetables.

TO PLATE: Pour sauce over the fish, serve with grilled vegetables and with sautéed sprouts.

Per Serving: 361 Calories; 16g Fat; 42g Protein; 15g Carbohydrate

Baked Catfish Fillets with Horseradish Sauce

2	pounds	catfish fillets (4)
3		egg whites
3	cups	lettuce leaves
2	cups	radicchio
3	cups	endives
2	tablespoons	lemon juice
1	head	garlic
4	tablespoons	Walden Farms Dressing
3	tablespoons	olive oil
2	tablespoons	prepared horseradish
1	tablespoon	onion powder
2	teaspoons	dry mustard
		sea salt to taste
		pepper to taste

Season fish with salt, pepper and 1/2 of the lemon juice. Drizzle with olive oil. Place in an oven-safe dish and bake at 375 degrees for 15 minutes or until cooked.

To roast the garlic, drizzle head with olive oil and bake in a 375-degree oven for about 30 minutes. Purée and allow to cool. Combine puree with mustard, horseradish and onion powder. Add whisked egg whites.
Using a hand blender, incorporate olive oil. Adjust seasoning with salt, pepper and lemon juice.

Serve with greens.

Per Serving: 351 Calories; 17g Fat; 41g Protein; 5g Carbohydrate

Baked Catfish with Okra

2	pounds	catfish
4	cups	okra fresh
2	packets	Ideal Protein Salt and Vinegar Ridges crushed
2	cups	green peppers cut in strips
2	cups	celery diagonally sliced
1	tablespoon	fresh basil chopped
1	tablespoon	Walden Farms Tomato and Basil Sauce
2	teaspoons	olive oil
1	teaspoon	dried basil crumbled
		sea salt to taste
		pepper to taste

Cook fresh okra in salted, boiling water for a few minutes. Drain.
Blanch celery in salted, boiling water. Add green peppers to water and cook until just tender. Drain.

Combine okra with Ridges and lightly sauté in olive oil.
Lightly grease a large baking dish and sprinkle with half of the crushed Ridges.
Add okra and fish.

Combine onion, Tomato and Basil sauce and basil. Spoon a layer over the fish. Sprinkle with peppers and celery and season with salt and pepper. Drizzle with olive oil and sprinkle remaining Ridges. Repeat layering until all ingredients are used.

Top with a layer of sautéed okra. Bake uncovered in a 300-degree oven for 1 hour.

Per Serving: 384 Calories; 11g Fat; 48g Protein; 22g Carbohydrate

Baked Haddock on Celery Purée

2	pounds haddock fillets		4	tablespoons olive oil
7	cups celery root diced 1/4" thick		1	tablespoon steak seasoning
2	tablespoons lemon juice			sea salt to taste
1	cup green onions chopped fine			pepper to taste
3	tablespoons parsley chopped fine			

Mix lemon juice, parsley and seasoning. Add fish and delicately mix. Set aside for 30 minutes.

Blanch celery root in salted, boiling water. Drain and dry. Mix with olive oil. Arrange in gratin dish in 1 layer. Top with marinated fish. Bake in a 375-degree oven.
Baste with marinade until fish and celery root are cooked.

Per Serving: 361 Calories; 15g Fat; 45g Protein; 10g Carbohydrate

Smoked Haddock Wraps with Greek Salad

1 3/4	pounds smoked haddock		2	cups green onions thinly sliced
1/2	pound calamari cooked		1/3	cup Walden Farms Caesar Dressing
2	cups cucumbers sliced 1/4" thick		1	tablespoon olive oil
2	cups spinach chopped			sea salt to taste
2	cups lettuce chopped			pepper to taste

Combine all the ingredients for the salad and mix with the Caesar dressing. Add cooked calamari.

Divide the smoked fish into 4 servings and arrange the pieces into squares with overlapping pieces. Spoon on salad in center and pile to the shape of a horn.
Lightly brush with olive oil. Place on a cold plate and garnish with a few leaves of spinach.

> **NOTE: If you cannot find smoked haddock, any other smoked white fish will do. You may also use any smoked spices to flavor your fish such as smoked paprika.**

Per Serving: 352 Calories; 6g Fat; 61g Protein; 8g Carbohydrate

Baked Haddock on
Celery Purée

Haddock Papillote

2	pounds	haddock fillets 4 pieces
3	cups	zucchini sliced 1/8" thick
3	cups	leek sliced
2		lemon zested and juiced
2	cups	green onions finely chopped
2	tablespoons	chives finely chopped
1	tablespoon	Walden Farms Tomato and Basil Sauce
2	tablespoons	olive oil
1	teaspoon	cider vinegar

SAUCE

1	teaspoon	lemon juice
2	tablespoons	Walden Farms Alfredo Sauce
1	tablespoon	olive oil
1	teaspoon	Dijon mustard
		sea salt to taste
		pepper to taste
		Aluminum Foil 4 10" x 10" squares

Preheat oven to 400 degrees.
In olive oil, slowly cook half of the leek. Add Tomato and Basil sauce. Simmer until leek is tender.

Slowly cook the other half of sliced leek in olive oil until tender. Allow to cool.
In each aluminum foil square equally divide leek and add a piece of fish. Add blanched zucchini, green onions and Tomato and Basil sauce. Drizzle with olive oil, cider vinegar, lemon zest and sprinkle with chives. Close the foil ensuring all sides are sealed tightly. Bake in oven for 20 minutes.

Mix Alfredo sauce and lemon juice. Combine with mustard and oil. Salt and pepper if necessary.

Per Serving: 364 Calories; 12g Fat; 46g Protein; 19g Carbohydrate

Sauté Red Snapper on a Bed of Spinach

2	pounds red snapper fillets
7	cups spinach
1	cup green onions
4	tablespoons Walden Farms Tomato and Basil Sauce
3	tablespoons olive oil
1	teaspoon cumin
	sea salt to taste
	pepper to taste

Sauté green onions and spinach in half of the olive oil. When water from the vegetables is completely evaporated, add Tomato and Basil sauce.

Season snapper with salt and cumin. Sauté in the other 1/2 of the olive oil until golden brown and lightly crisped.

Serve fish on a bed of spinach.

> **NOTE: You can use any kind of Walden Farms Sauce to flavor the dish, depending on your mood.**

Per Serving: 352 Calories; 13g Fat; 49g Protein; 4g Carbohydrate

Blackened Red Snapper

2	pounds snapper fillets
8	cups leek sliced
1	tablespoon olive oil
2	teaspoons onion powder
1	teaspoon garlic powder
1	teaspoon dry mustard
1	teaspoon ground thyme
2	teaspoons chili pepper
	sea salt to taste
	pepper to taste

Combine onion powder, garlic powder, dry mustard, ground thyme, pepper and chili. Cover one side of each fillet with half of this mixture. Coat a large cast iron skillet with cooking spray and place over medium high heat until hot. Add fillets, seasoned side down and cook 4 minutes. Sprinkle fillets with remaining spices. Turn over and cook 3 minutes or until fillets are blackened and flake easily when tested with a fork. Slowly sauté leek in olive oil until tender.

Arrange on plate and top with fish.

Per Serving: 375 Calories; 7g Fat; 50g Protein; 27g Carbohydrate;

Fish and seafood

Red Snapper Fillet on a Fennel and Cucumber Salad

2	pounds	red snapper 4 fillets
4	cups	cucumber finely sliced
4	cups	fennel finely sliced
4	teaspoons	lemon juice
1	teaspoon	sea salt for cucumbers

SALAD DRESSING

2	tablespoons	fresh mint finely chopped
2	tablespoons	parsley finely chopped
1	tablespoon	Walden Farms Orange Spread chopped
2 1/2	tablespoons	olive oil
1/2	cup	cider vinegar
1/8	teaspoon	paprika
		sea salt to taste
		pepper to taste

Sprinkle 1 teaspoon of salt on cucumbers and refrigerate for 1 hour.
Lightly rinse under cold water and dry well.

Combine cucumber, fennel and lemon juice in a bowl. Set aside.
Mix ingredients for the salad dressing with a whisk. Salt and pepper to taste.
Pour half over vegetables and mix well. Refrigerate for 1 to 2 hours.

Season and sauté fish fillets in olive oil on low heat. Keep warm.
Plate the vegetable salad on cold plates and top with warm fish.
Drizzle with the remaining salad dressing.

Per Serving: 350 Calories; 12g Fat; 49g Protein; 12g Carbohydrate

Cod and Fennel Papillotes

2	pounds cod fillets	2	tablespoons olive oil
6	cups fennel bulbs thinly sliced	1	tablespoon fish sauce
2	cups green pepper thinly sliced	1	tablespoon cumin
2	tablespoons dill branches	1	tablespoon anise seed
1	pinch saffron		sea salt to taste
			pepper to taste

In a pan, heat olive oil then add fennel and cook slowly. Add peppers and anise seeds and cook until tender. Set aside.

Divide half of the dill branches equally on four sheets of aluminum foil. Add vegetables and cod fillets. Drizzle olive oil over each filet and garnish with remaining dill and saffron. Season.

Fold foil to make tightly sealed envelopes. Cook the envelopes on the barbecue over medium-high heat or in the oven at 350 degrees for 8 to 10 minutes or until fish "flakes" easily.

> **NOTE: The saffron will color this dish in a warm yellow tone.**

Per Serving: 352 Calories; 10g Fat; 44g Protein; 18g Carbohydrate

Grilled Cod With Vegetables

2	pounds cod fillets 4 pieces	1	clove garlic crushed
3	cups leek finely sliced	4	tablespoons olive oil
2	cups zucchini finely sliced	1	tablespoon sesame seeds
2	cups mushrooms finely sliced		sea salt to taste
1	cup green onions finely sliced		pepper to taste

Shape two layers of foil over the outside of a 1" baking dish. Once shaped, remove foil and crimp the edges to form a tight rim, making a "mock" pan with 1" sides. Coat foil pan with olive oil. Place on a cookie sheet. Place cod fillets in center of foil pan.

Warm olive oil and add leek to frying pan, sauté slowly. Once tender, place with fish in foil pan.

In same fry pan, sauté mushrooms with zucchini and green onions. Add garlic and sesame seeds.
Spoon the tender vegetables evenly around the fish. Drizzle fish and vegetables with olive oil. Season.
Cook 15 to 18 minutes, covered, on a medium-hot grill or until fish flakes easily when tested with a fork.

Per Serving: 385 Calories; 17g Fat; 44g Protein; 15g Carbohydrate

Cod and Fennel Papillotes

Fish Medley Lasagna

1	pound halibut cooked		2	cups celery chopped
1/2	pound cod		2	cups green onions minced
1/2	pound swordfish		4	lemon wedges to garnish
1	packet Ideal Protein Pancakes prepared			sea salt to taste
2	packets Ideal Protein Mushroom Soup prepared			pepper to taste
4	cups spinach			

Preheat oven to 375 degrees.
Slowly cook celery and green onions in 1 teaspoon of olive oil. Add spinach and reduce water (if needed). Add 1/4 of the mushroom soup. Set aside.

Ensure Pancakes are approximately the size of the baking dish.
Arrange a layer of pancakes, fish and vegetable preparation. Add another pancake and continue to layer. Proceed until dish is full. Top with the remaining mushroom soup.
Bake until hot inside.
Decorate with lemon wedges.

Per Serving: 353 Calories; 6g Fat; 61g Protein; 12g Carbohydrate

....

Flounder on Fennel with Tomato and Basil Sauce

2	pounds flounder fresh or frozen		3	tablespoons Walden Farms Tomato and Basil Sauce
8	cups fennel finely sliced		3	tablespoons olive oil
1	teaspoon parsley chopped fine			sea salt to taste
1	teaspoon basil chopped fine			pepper to taste

In a pan, heat olive oil, add fennel and cover. Cook slowly. Fennel should be tender but not browned. Add water if necessary.
Place fennel in 4 heaps in a baking dish. Top with herbs and seasoned fish. Drizzle with olive oil. Bake in a 400-degree oven for 8 to 10 minutes or until fish is cooked.
Remove from oven and transfer cooking juice to small pan. Reduce by half. Add Tomato and Basil sauce and adjust seasoning.
Arrange fish on fennel heaps and pour over sauce.

Per Serving: 351 Calories; 13g Fat; 45g Protein; 13g Carbohydrate

Fish Medley Lasagna

Last Minute Tuna Plate

2	pounds	tuna in water, canned drained
2	packages	Ideal Protein Leek Soup prepared
2	cups	green onions finely chopped
2	cups	celery thinly sliced
2	cups	green pepper thinly sliced
1	teaspoon	onion powder
2	cups	mushroom drained
1	teaspoon	olive oil
		sea salt to taste
		pepper to taste

Sauté vegetables in olive oil. Once tender, add soup. Bring to boil. Add drained tuna. Reheat and serve.

Per Serving: 374 Calories; 4g Fat; 70g Protein; 14g Carbohydrate

....

Sole Florentine

2 1/2	pounds	sole fillets
6	cups	spinach
2	cups	green onions finely sliced
1	cup	Walden Farms Shrimp Sauce
2	tablespoons	olive oil
		paprika to taste
		sea salt to taste
		pepper to taste

Heat olive oil. Add green onions and spinach. Season with salt, pepper and paprika. Place into an oven-safe dish.

Fold the seasoned fish fillets and lay each on top of the spinach. Cover and bake for 10 minutes in a 375-degree oven.

Drain the juice from the dish into a small pan and reduce to one teaspoon. Add shrimp sauce and return to a boil to complete heating.

Serve spinach on a plate. Top with fish and drizzle with sauce.

Per Serving: 352 Calories; 10g Fat; 56g Protein; 5g Carbohydrate

Last Minute Tuna Plate

Marinated Tilapia on a Bed of Fennel Salad

1 1/2	pounds tilapia		4	tablespoons Walden Farms Seafood Sauce
4	cups soybean sprouts blanched		1	tablespoon olive oil
3 1/2	cups fennel bulb finely sliced		1	tablespoon onion powder
3	limes		1	teaspoon sea salt
2	tablespoons green onions			red pepper flakes to taste
2	tablespoons parsley finely chopped			sea salt to taste
2	tablespoons coriander leaves			pepper to taste

Combine the tilapia with the juice of 1 lime and sea salt. Marinate in the refrigerator for 1 hour. This will cook the tilapia. Wash and dry on paper towels. Set aside in the freezer for 15 minutes. This will allow for easier slicing.

Blanch the fennel in salted, boiling water. Set aside and preserve the cooking water. Cut fish into thick strips. Arrange on a shallow baking dish. Add green onions, Seafood sauce and mix. Add the juice of 1 lime and 3 tablespoons of the cooking water from the fennel. Cover with plastic wrap and marinate in the fridge for 2 hours. Stir every 30 minutes.

Slice the 3rd lime into thin slices.
Mix fennel with sprouts and olive oil.
Plate fish on very cold plates over the fennel salad. Salt and pepper to taste. Add red pepper powder and decorate with lime slices.

> **NOTE: You can use wild salmon for this recipe. In this case, it would be a restricted food to be consumed once a week only. Make sure to use wild salmon, 90% of the salmon on the market is farm-fed salmon, which is fattier than wild salmon. Salmon is an excellent source of Omega 3 especially if served raw.**

Per Serving: 351 Calories; 12g Fat; 46g Protein; 20g Carbohydrate

Tilapia Malawi Style

2	pounds tilapia		3	tablespoons olive oil
4	cups fennel quartered		2	teaspoons hot chili powder
4	cups green peppers quartered			sea salt to taste
3	teaspoons lemon juice			pepper to taste

Make fine cuts on the fish, and apply a mixture of salt, hot chili powder and lemon.
Grill or roast on a skewer near an open fire pit.
Blanch fennel in boiling salted water.

Season fennel and green peppers and grill like the fish. Add some olive oil.
Grill or bake in oven.

Per Serving: 368 Calories; 13g Fat; 45g Protein; 17g Carbohydrate

....

Okra and Walleye Pike Fricassee

1 1/2	pounds walleye pike fillets		3	tablespoons oil
6	cups okra 1/2" cubes		1	teaspoon red chili flakes
2	cups green onions finely chopped		1/4	teaspoon turmeric
1	tablespoon jalapeño finely chopped		1	teaspoon cumin powder
1	teaspoon garlic crushed			sea salt to taste
1/2	cup Walden Farms Chipotle Dressing			pepper to taste

Heat oil in a non-stick skillet. Add green onions and fry until light golden brown.
Add garlic and fry for an additional minute.

Add okra and jalapeños. Fry on high heat for 3 minutes. Add salt and turmeric.
Lower heat to medium. Add walleye pike fillets, dressing and heat until fish is cooked.
Sprinkle cumin seed powder and remove from heat.

NOTE: You may use any white fresh water fish for this recipe.

Per Serving: 351 Calories; 13g Fat; 39g Protein; 16g Carbohydrate

Pickerel in Sweet 'n' Sour Sauce

2	pounds pickerel		2	tablespoons Walden Farms Honey BBQ Sauce
2	cups fish stock			
4	cups Chinese cabbage finely sliced		2	tablespoons Walden Farms Ketchup
2	cups green peppers finely sliced			
2	cups green onions finely sliced		4	tablespoons cider vinegar
1	tablespoon sesame oil			sea salt to taste
2	tablespoons garlic crushed			pepper to taste
2	tablespoons fresh ginger finely sliced			

Sauté peppers and green onions in sesame oil. Add cabbage and cook until vegetables are tender. Remove vegetables and set aside.

Using the same pan, bring ketchup and BBQ sauce to a boil. Add vinegar and boil until the sauce reduces to 4 tablespoon. Add fish stock and simmer for 5 minutes. Add fish and simmer until cooked.

Remove fish and reheat the vegetables in this sauce (if sauce is too thick, add water accordingly). Adjust seasoning.

Serve fish on top of the vegetables. Drizzle the sauce around the vegetable and fish.

Per Serving: 383 Calories; 12g Fat; 50g Protein; 14g Carbohydrate

------

Wasabi Shark Skewers

2	pounds shark steak cubed		1	cup Walden Farms Seafood Sauce
3	cups portobello mushrooms without stems		3	tablespoons soy sauce
3	cups green peppers		1	tablespoon Wasabi powder
2	tablespoons green onions chopped fine			sea salt to taste
				pepper to taste
1	tablespoon fresh ginger chopped fine		4	skewers prepared

Bring 1/2 cup of water to a boil. Add ginger and soy sauce. Cool. Add fish and mushrooms. Add peppers. Refrigerate for 2 to 3 hours. Drain.
Prepare skewers and cook on a hot barbecue or under broiler.

Prepare the dipping sauce. Mix Wasabi powder, green onions and Seafood sauce.

Per Serving: 379 Calories; 11g Fat; 53g Protein; 17g Carbohydrate

Honey Mustard Shark Steaks in Cabbage

2	pounds shark steaks		1	tablespoon olive oil
6	cups cabbage		2	tablespoons Dijon mustard
2	cups green onions finely chopped			sea salt to taste
2	teaspoons thyme			pepper to taste
4	tablespoons Walden Farms Honey Dijon Dressing			

Remove 8 big leaves of cabbage and blanch in salted, boiling water. Chop the remaining cabbage.

Mix dressing with mustard. Marinate fish in this preparation for 1 hour.

Sauté 1 cup of green onions in olive oil. Add chopped cabbage and thyme. Cook slowly. When tender, add 1/2 cup of water and transfer to a baking dish.
Add shark to cabbage and continue cooking basting shark with mustard and dressing marinade. Cover and simmer in a 350-degree oven until completely cooked (30 to 40 minutes).

Top blanched cabbage leaves with half of the cabbage and shark preparation. Add the other cup of green onions. Wrap cabbage leaves to completely cover the fish. Baste with olive oil and cook in a 350-degree oven for 15 minutes.

Per Serving: 381 Calories; 14g Fat; 51g Protein; 12g Carbohydrate

Simple Curry Shark

2	pounds shark steaks
3	cups celery root finely chopped
3	cups fennel
2	cups green onions finely chopped
1	teaspoon olive oil
1	tablespoon curry paste
	sea salt to taste
	pepper to taste

Sear shark in olive oil. Add green onions, fennel and celery. Add curry paste and just enough water to cover the vegetables. Simmer until fish is cooked.

Per Serving: 376 Calories; 14g Fat; 50g Protein; 12g Carbohydrate

Fish and seafood

Honey Mustard Shark Steaks
in Cabbage

Spinach Salad with Shrimp and Quail Eggs

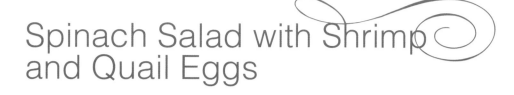

2	pounds shrimp cooked
12	quail eggs hard-boiled and sliced
6	cups spinach leaves
2	cups radicchio sliced
1	tablespoon cider vinegar
3	tablespoons olive oil
1	tablespoon Dijon mustard
	sea salt to taste
	pepper to taste

To hard-boil eggs: Boil water. Add eggs. Lower temperature to simmer.
Cook for 5 minutes. Remove. Allow to cool.

DRESSING: Dissolve the mustard with vinegar, salt and pepper.
Add the olive slowly mixing very well.

Place spinach in salad bowl, add salad dressing, mix and plate. Add radicchio.
Top with shrimp surround with sliced eggs.

NOTE: You can replace quail eggs with 8 whole chicken eggs.

Per Serving: 391 Calories; 17g Fat; 51g Protein; 5g Carbohydrate

....

Shrimps in Creamy Blue Cheese Spinach

2 1/2	pounds shrimp fresh, peeled and deveined
7	cups spinach
1	cup green onions
1	cup Walden Farms Blue Cheese Dressing
1	tablespoon olive oil
1	pinch ground nutmeg
	sea salt to taste
	pepper to taste

Cook shrimps in olive oil until pink. Add spinach. Cook until liquid has evaporated.
Add nutmeg and dressing. Cook for another 3 minutes.
Serve very hot.

Per Serving: 350 Calories; 8g Fat; 59g Protein; 6g Carbohydrate

fish and seafood

Spinach Salad with Shrimp
and Quail Eggs

Curry Shrimp

1 1/2	pounds shrimp fresh, peeled and deveined
8	cups green peppers cut 1" thick
1	clove garlic crushed
2	tablespoons olive oil
2	tablespoons curry paste
	sea salt to taste
	pepper to taste

Heat olive oil in pan at low temperature. Add peppers and cook for 2 minutes. Mix in curry and garlic.

Add shrimp in single layer only. Cook for 3 to 5 minutes on each side until pink. Plate and add the remaining curry sauce.

Per Serving: 364 Calories; 14g Fat; 38g Protein; 22g Carbohydrate

Sweet and Sour Shrimp

2	pounds shrimp fresh, peeled and deveined	3	tablespoons chili sauce
1 1/2	cups alfalfa sprouts	1	tablespoon oil
2 1/2	cups green onion sliced 1/4" thick	3	tablespoons cider vinegar
2	fennel bulbs	1	teaspoon garlic powder
2	cups green pepper chopped		sea salt to taste
2	tablespoons Walden Farms Fruit Spread chopped		pepper to taste
2	tablespoons soy sauce		

Mix fruit spread with chili sauce, soy sauce and garlic powder. Set aside.
Over medium temperature, heat oil in a large skillet. Stir-fry pepper and fennel for 2 to 3 minutes. Add shrimp; cook an additional 3 minutes or until shrimps turn pink. Add green onions. Remove cooked ingredients and set aside.

In same pan, add fruit spread mixture and vinegar. Cook, stirring constantly, until sauce thickens and bubbles. Return shrimp and vegetable mixture. Add half of the alfalfa sprouts at the last minute, stir and serve.
Garnish plate with the other half of sprouts.

> **NOTE: Alfalfa may be served raw or may be replaced by bean sprouts (lightly sautéed).**

Per Serving: 352 Calories; 8g Fat; 49g Protein; 17g Carbohydrate

Spicy Shrimps Oriental Style

2	pounds shrimp fresh, peeled and deveined	1	tablespoon Walden Farms Ketchup
1/2	pound scallops peas sized pieces	1	teaspoon soy sauce
4	cups broccoli florets	2	teaspoons sesame oil
2	cups zucchini cut in 1" pieces	1	teaspoon cider vinegar
2	cups green onions sliced	1	chili pepper
2	teaspoons minced garlic		sea salt to taste
1	teaspoon fresh ginger or ground ginger		pepper to taste
2	tablespoons Walden Farms Seafood Sauce		

Combine vinegar, soy sauce, ginger, garlic chili pepper and shrimp and refrigerate for 1 hour. Warm the sesame oil. Sauté shrimp and add scallops. Remove from pan. Add marinade to the pan and reduce. Add cooked sauce and 2 tablespoons of water. Cook until desired consistency. Adjust seasoning if necessary.
Blanch broccoli in salted, boiling water.

Cook green onions and zucchini in sesame oil. When tender, add broccoli cut into small florets. Adjust seasoning (salt, ginger, hot pepper).
Return seafood to sauce. Serve very hot beside the vegetables.

> **NOTE: Remember that scallops cook faster than shrimp, adjust cooking time accordingly.**

Per Serving: 362 Calories; 7g Fat; 59g Protein; 14g Carbohydrate

Cajun Shrimp Meatloaf

1	pound halibut ground	1/2	cup Walden Farms Tomato and Basil Sauce
1/2	pound shrimp cooked	3	tablespoons olive oil
3	egg whites wisked	1	tablespoon cider vinegar
1/3	cup Ideal Protein Salt and Vinegar Ridges	1	teaspoon hot sauce
3	cups radicchio leaves	1	teaspoon Dijon mustard
2	cups green pepper chopped	1 1/2	teaspoons Cajun seasoning
2	cups green onions chopped		sea salt to taste
1	cup celery chopped		pepper to taste
1/2	cup Walden Farms Alfredo Sauce		

Preheat oven to 350 degrees. Combine ground fish in a large bowl and add egg whites, sauces and shrimp. Add finely chopped vegetables. Once all ingredients are combined, shape into loaf. Place loaf on a baking dish in a oven for 30 minutes or until the center is cooked. Serve a slice of meatloaf on a bed of radicchio leaves.

> **NOTE: You can replace shrimp with crayfish, if available.**

Per Serving: 413 Calories; 16g Fat; 46g Protein; 22g Carbohydrate

Chilled Shrimp Gazpacho

2	pounds shrimp fresh, peeled and deveined		3	tablespoons picante sauce
4	cups cucumber chopped		2	tablespoons olive oil
4	cups green pepper chopped		4	tablespoons cider vinegar
1/2	teaspoon tarragon			sea salt to taste
1/2	teaspoon thyme			pepper to taste
1	cup Walden Farms Tomato and Basil Sauce			

Boil 3 cups of water in medium saucepan. Add shrimp. Cook 3 to 5 minutes or until pink. Drain and rinse with cold water.

Purée half of the vegetables with Tomato and Basil sauce. Add some of the shrimps cooking liquid as needed (this is the soup base).

Add the other half of the vegetables to a large bowl with cooked shrimps. Add vegetable purée, herbs, olive oil and hot sauce. Add vinegar. Mix well. Cover and chill for at least 1 hour. Serve in a bowl and top with shrimp.

> **NOTE: This cold soup is an excellent soup for summertime.**

Per Serving: 361 Calories; 11g Fat; 48g Protein; 16g Carbohydrate

Ginger Shrimp

2	pounds shrimp fresh, peeled and deveined		1/4	cup cider vinegar
6	cups mung bean sprouts		1/4	cup soy sauce
2	teaspoons fresh ginger finely chopped		2	tablespoons Tamari soy sauce
2	cups green onions finely chopped			sea salt to taste
1	tablespoon sesame oil			pepper to taste

Bring 4 cups of water to a boil. Add soy sauce and ginger and continue to cook for 5 minutes on medium heat. Add vinegar and salt.

Add shrimp. Return to a boil and remove from the stove. Refrigerate for 2 to 3 hours (shrimps will finish cooking while cooling down).

Sauté soybean sprouts in sesame oil for 3 minutes. Add 2 tablespoons of the shrimp cooking liquid. Reduce.

Serve shrimps on a bed of sprouts.

> **NOTE: if shrimps are very large allow them to simmer for 2 minutes before letting them cool down.**

Per Serving: 351 Calories; 8g Fat; 53g Protein; 18g Carbohydrate

Chilled Shrimp Gazpacho

Crab Salad with Cocktail Sauce

2	pounds crab meat cooked		3	tablespoons Walden Farms Mayonnaise
1	package Ideal Protein Salt and		1	tablespoon Walden Farms Ketchup
	Vinegar Ridges		2	tablespoons olive oil
8	cups mixed greens		1	tablespoon cider vinegar
4	tablespoons lime juice			ground pepper to taste
1	tablespoon tarragon chopped fine			sea salt to taste
1	tablespoon parsley			

Mix crab meat with just enough mayonnaise and ketchup to cover. Add lime juice, salt and a generous amount of ground pepper. Mix well. Set aside.
Mix the cider vinegar and olive oil, combine with the greens.
Divide greens in small serving bowls and spoon crab meat mixture into each. Sprinkle Ridges, chopped tarragon and parsley over each cocktail and serve.

Per Serving: 362 Calories; 11g Fat; 54g Protein; 11g Carbohydrate

Crab Cabbage Parcel with Blueberry Szechuan Sauce

2	pounds crabmeat flaked		1	teaspoon lime juice
1	packet Ideal Protein		1	teaspoon ginger grated
	Salt and Vinegar Ridges crushed		2	cloves garlic minced
4	cups spinach		1/2	cup Walden Farms
2	cups green pepper			Blueberry Spread chopped
2	tablespoons lemon juice		2	tablespoons Walden Farms
3	tablespoons olive oil			Honey BBQ Sauce
2	cups cabbage leaves			sea salt to taste
				pepper to taste

SAUCE: Mix BBQ sauce, spread, ginger, lime juice and garlic. Bring to a boil. Refrigerate for a few hours.

FILLING: Wash spinach. With leaves still wet, place in large pan over medium-high heat. Cook until spinach just begins to wilt and most of the water has evaporated. Remove from pan and chop finely. Set aside.
Sauté green peppers in olive oil. Reduce to low heat. Add lemon juice. Mix. Remove from heat and add crab, Ridges and spinach.

Blanch cabbage leaves in salted, boiling water. Place each leaf flat on cutting board and spoon in filling. Wrap well. Place in oiled baking dish and top with sauce. Bake in a 400-degree oven until very hot. Serve with the remaining sauce.

Per Serving: 371 Calories; 14g Fat; 47g Protein; 13g Carbohydrate

Crab Salad with Cocktail Sauce

Crab Stuffed Mushrooms

2	pounds	crab meat cooked, flaked
12	large	porcini mushrooms
2	cups	spinach washed
3	cups	portobello mushrooms
2	tablespoons	green onions finely chopped
1	tablespoon	basil finely chopped
2	teaspoons	lemon juice
1	cup	Walden Farms Seafood Sauce
2	dashes	Worcestershire sauce
1	tablespoon	olive oil
2	teaspoons	garlic powder
		sea salt to taste
		pepper to taste

Peel and clean the Porcini mushrooms. Remove stems and baste caps with olive oil. Grill for a few minutes and set aside.
Chop the stems along with the Portobello mushrooms.

In the remaining olive oil, cook green onions on low temperature. Add the chopped mushrooms, garlic powder, salt and pepper. Increase heat to medium and add spinach. Cook until liquid is evaporated.

Combine the sauces, basil, lemon and crab meat.
Fill the mushroom caps with crab mixture.

Bake at 450 degrees for 15 to 20 minutes and serve warm.

Per Serving: 351 Calories; 7g Fat; 52g Protein; 19g Carbohydrate

Scallops in a Creamy Tomato Sauce with Spinach

2 1/4	pounds scallops	2	cups Walden Farms Tomato and Basil Sauce
5	cups spinach		
3	cups oyster mushrooms sliced	3	tablespoons olive oil
1	cup green onions		sea salt to taste
1	tablespoon garlic crushed		pepper to taste

Dry the scallops. Season. Very quickly, sear scallops in heated olive oil. They must be golden but not overcooked. Remove from pan and keep warm.
Using the same pan, add oil if needed, and add mushrooms. Sauté until brown. Season.
Add green onions, spinach. Remove and set aside.

Using the same pan bring the Tomato and Basil sauce to a boil. Season.
On each plate, make a bed of spinach and top with scallops.
Drizzle sauce.

Per Serving: 353 Calories; 12g Fat; 46g Protein; 13g Carbohydrate

Scallops with Raspberry Sauce

2	pounds scallops
8	cups fennel bulb cut 1" thick
1	cup Walden Farms Raspberry Vinaigrette Dressing
2	tablespoons Walden Farms Honey Dijon Dressing
3	tablespoons olive oil
	sea salt to taste
	pepper to taste

Mix dressings, olive oil and pepper.
Place scallops in a container and add 3/4 of the dressing. Mix delicately and refrigerate for 30 minutes.

Place scallops on skewers and sauté at high temperature for 2-3 minutes. Remove.
Add fennel to the same pan and cook until tender.

Heat remaining marinade and serve over fennel.

Per Serving: 352 Calories; 12g Fat; 40g Protein; 18g Carbohydrate

Fish and seafood

Scallops in a Creamy Tomato
Sauce with Spinach

Scallops Sauté with Jalapeño Tart

2	pounds	scallops, large
6	egg whites	slightly beaten
1	packet	Ideal Protein Pancakes –made into batter not cooked
4	cups	spinach cut into 1 1/2" pieces
4	cups	enoki mushrooms
1 1/2	tablespoons	jalapeños chopped
1/2	cup	Walden Farms Alfredo Sauce
1/4	cup	Walden Farms Blue Cheese Dip
2	tablespoons	olive oil
	sea salt	to taste
	pepper	to taste

Line 4 small tartlet pans with pancake batter. Brush with 1 egg white.
Bake tart shell in preheated 450-degree oven for 10 minutes or just until lightly browned, (to dry them).

Sauté enoki mushrooms and spinach in olive oil; drain excess water.

Remove baked shell from oven and reduce temperature to 375 degrees.
Top with spinach, mushrooms and jalapeños.

In medium bowl, combine 5 egg whites with Alfredo sauce and dip.
Salt and pepper to taste. Pour mixture into tart shell over vegetables.

Bake in preheated oven for 35 to 50 minutes, or until knife inserted in center comes out clean. Let stand 5 minutes before serving.

Sauté seasoned scallops in hot olive oil. Drain. Serve next to the tartlets.

Per Serving: 350 Calories; 9g Fat; 50g Protein; 15g Carbohydrate

Scallops and Zucchini Casserole

2	pounds scallops large
1 1/2	packets Ideal Protein Salt and Vinegar Ridges crushed
8	cups zucchini sliced lengthwise
2	cups Walden Farms Tomato and Basil Sauce
1 1/2	cups Walden Farms Mayonnaise
3	tablespoons olive oil
	sea salt to taste
	pepper to taste

Sauté zucchini in olive oil. Remove from heat. Baste each side with mayonnaise and dip into the Ridges. Place on cookie sheet and bake at 400 degrees for 10 minutes.
Sauté scallops for a few seconds on each side.

Layer zucchini slices in a shallow baking dish. Add a scallop lyer and make a second layer of zucchinis. Cover with Tomato and Basil sauce. Bake at 350 degrees for 15 minutes. Scallops should be cooked but still lightly translucent in the middle.

Per Serving: 384 Calories; 14g Fat; 47g Protein; 18g Carbohydrate

Szechuan Style Scallops

2	pounds scallops	2	teaspoons sesame oil
4	cups soybean sprouts	2	tablespoons soy sauce
2	cups green peppers chopped	1/2	teaspoon ground ginger
2	cups green onions chopped	1/2	teaspoon Szechuan pepper
4	tablespoons Walden Farms Tomato and Basil Sauce	1	teaspoon hot red pepper flakes
2	tablespoons Walden Farms Seafood Sauce		sea salt to taste
			pepper to taste

Prepare all ingredients near stovetop. Heat large wok. Add sesame oil.
Add green peppers and bean sprouts. Cook over medium heat until vegetables are just crispy. Add peppers, soy sauce and other sauces.

Cover and bring to a simmer for 5 minutes. Uncover and simmer until sauce reduces (approx.4 to 5 minutes). Stir in scallops and cook until they are heated through and coated with sauce.

NOTE: You can replace the Szechuan pepper with 1/4 teaspoon of regular pepper.

Per Serving: 353 Calories; 9g Fat; 49g Protein; 21g Carbohydrate

Calamari on a Catalan Vegetable Gratin

1 1/2	pounds	calamari sliced 1/3" thick
9	whole	anchovies
1	packet	Ideal Protein Salt and Vinegar Ridges crushed
4	cups	zucchini cut 1/4" thick
4	cups	green peppers
2	teaspoons	oregano
2	tablespoons	parsley
1/2	cup	Walden Farms Tomato and Basil Sauce
3	tablespoons	olive oil
		sea salt to taste
		pepper to taste

Sprinkle zucchini with salt and set aside for 1 hour.
Cut peppers in half and baste with olive oil. Place under broiler until roasted (browned) on both sides. Run under cold water and remove skin. Cut into 1/4" thick pieces.
In a pan, heat 1 tablespoon of olive oil. Add Ridges and sauté for a few minutes. Salt and pepper. Add oregano and parsley.

Rinse zucchini and dry on a paper towel. Heat 1 tablespoon of olive oil. Sauté until browned.

In an oval baking dish, layer zucchini and top with a layer of peppers. Repeat.
Bake in a 350-degree oven for 10 to 15 minutes.

In a hot pan, quickly sauté calamari in 1/2 tablespoon of olive oil. Add Ridges mixture.
Place on top of vegetable gratin just before serving.
Serve warm or at room temperature.

NOTE: Letting zucchini sit for 1 hour with salt helps extract water and increases the taste.

Per Serving: 366 Calories; 15g Fat; 36g Protein; 22g Carbohydrate

Steamed Mussels with Wasabi

2	pounds mussels		1	teaspoon olive oil
6	cups soybean sprouts		1	tablespoon soy sauce
2	cups leek chopped		1	teaspoon wasabi
1	tablespoon lemon juice			sea salt to taste
1	tablespoon ginger finely chopped			pepper to taste
1	teaspoon coriander finely chopped			

Slowly cook leek in olive oil for 5 minutes. Add ginger and cook for an additional minute. Add mussels, 1 cup of water, lemon juice, soy sauce and wasabi. Bring to a boil, turn heat off.

Serve the washed soybean sprouts in a large bowl, add the boiling juice of the mussels. Add mussels. Sprinkle with coriander.

NOTE: If you enjoy the flavor of wasabi, you may add an additional teaspoon.

Per Serving: 369 Calories; 13g Fat; 42g Protein; 26g Carbohydrate

Poached Oysters and Mussels on a Zucchini Saffron Fricassee

48	oysters fresh		2	tablespoons olive oil
2	pounds mussels		3	pinches saffron
6	cups zucchini sliced 1/4" thick		1	tablespoon onion powder
2	cups green peppers chopped fine		1/2	teaspoon cayenne pepper
1/2	cup parsley chopped fine			sea salt to taste
				pepper to taste

Infuse saffron in 2 teaspoons of warm water.
Sauté zucchini and peppers in olive oil with onion powder and cayenne pepper. Add half of the saffron water. Reduce. Salt and pepper to taste.
Sprinkle parsley just before serving.

Place mussels in a pan with the rest of saffron water and an additional 1/2 cup of water. Cover and bring to boil.
When all mussels are open, remove from pan. Use same pan to poach the oysters for one minute. Already opened oysters may be used if preferred.
Remove mussels from their shells. Reheat mussels and oysters in mussel juice and serve on top of the zucchini fricassee.

NOTE: Do not over-poach oysters. Only heat slightly.

Per Serving: 379 Calories; 15g Fat; 37g Protein; 24g Carbohydrate;

Steamed Mussels with Wasabi

Cumin Seafood Stir-Fry

1	pound cod cut in 1 1/2" chunks
1/2	pound crab meat cooked
1/2	pound shrimp fresh, peeled and deveined
1	cup fish stock
3	green pepper finely chopped
3	cups mushrooms sliced
2	cups green onions
2	tablespoons lemon juice
2	tablespoons parsley finely chopped
1	teaspoon thyme crushed
1 1/2	cups Walden Farms Alfredo Sauce
2	tablespoons olive oil
1	teaspoon cumin
	sea salt to taste
	pepper to taste

Sear fish and shrimp in olive oil. Set aside.
Using the same pan, sauté green onions with mushrooms. Add green peppers and cumin seeds. Add lemon juice and fish stock. Bring to a boil and simmer for 5 minutes.
Add Alfredo sauce. (Reduce if needed, until the sauce coats a spoon).
Add fish, shrimp and crab. Finish simmering on low temperature.

Just before serving add parsley, thyme, salt and pepper.
Serve in a soup bowl.

Per Serving: 352 Calories; 11g Fat; 46g Protein; 14g Carbohydrate

Zucchini and Seafood Gratin

1	pound calamari sliced
1	pound shrimp cooked
8	egg whites
7	cups zucchini finely sliced
1	cup green onions finely chopped
2	cloves garlic finely chopped
2	tablespoons olive oil
1	teaspoon herbs de Provence
1	pinch saffron threads
12	basil leaves chopped
	sea salt to taste
	pepper to taste

Soak saffron in a teaspoon of warm water and set aside.
Sprinkle salt over zucchini and set aside on a baker's rack for 1 hour. Wash and dry.
Sauté zucchini in olive oil and set aside. In the same oil, sauté the calamari for 1 minute, remove the calamari, and fry 4 basil leaves.

Purée half of the zucchini in food processor and season if desired. Add basil.
Prepare an oiled gratin dish. Arrange a layer of zucchini and spread with green onions shrimps and calamari. Top with garlic and herbs de Provence. Add another layer of zucchini, sprinkle with onions and garlic. Continue until all vegetables are used.

Wisk the egg whites with the saffron and water. Incorporate the mixture into the zucchini purée. Pour over vegetables. Bake in 425-degree oven for 10 minutes or until egg whites are cooked.

Per Serving: 359 Calories; 11g Fat; 51g Protein; 14g Carbohydrate; 3g Dietary Fiber; 437mg Cholesterol; 338mg Sodium.

Orange Asparagus Seafood Stir-Fry

1 1/2	pounds shrimp fresh, peeled and deveined
3/4	pound scallops
6	cups asparagus cut diagonally into 2" pieces
2	cups green onions
1/2	cup Walden Farms Orange Spread chopped
1 1/2	tablespoons olive oil divided
	sea salt to taste
	pepper to taste

Warm 1 tablespoon of olive oil over high heat in a large non-stick wok or skillet. Stir-fry the shrimp and scallops until firm, opaque and lightly browned (approx. 3 minutes). Remove and set aside. Add the remaining teaspoon of olive oil to the pan and stir-fry asparagus and scallions. Add 1/2 cup of water and simmer for another 3 to 4 minutes until asparagus are tender and crisp. Add spread and 1/2 cup of water. Bring to a boil. Reduce and add shrimp and scallops until warmed.

Per Serving: 361 Calories; 9g Fat; 54g Protein; 16g Carbohydrate

Szechuan Style Frog Legs and Broccoli

2 1/2	pounds frog legs	2	tablespoons olive oil
8	cups broccoli	2	tablespoons cider vinegar
1	tablespoon fresh ginger finely chopped	2	teaspoons green peppercorns crushed
6	cloves garlic crushed		sea salt to taste
2	tablespoons Walden Farms Caramel Syrup		pepper to taste
3	tablespoons soy sauce		

Blanch broccoli in salted, boiling water for 5 minutes. Cool. Set aside.
Combine 2 tablespoons of soy sauce, vinegar and caramel syrup in bowl and set aside.
Heat skillet. Add oil, pepper, half of the ginger and half of the garlic for 30 seconds. Add broccoli. Cook for 1 minute. Add soy mixture. Cover and cook for 2 minutes.
Sauté frog legs in oil. Add chopped garlic, the rest of fresh ginger and soy sauce. Reduce until syrupy consistency is achieved.

Per Serving: 352 Calories; 8g Fat; 52g Protein; 12g Carbohydrate

Soups, Salads & Eggs Index

Poultry Index

Meat Index

Fish and Seafood Index